Hurry Up
Nurse 3

DAWN BROOKES

Hurry Up Nurse 3

More adventures in the life of a student nurse

DAWN BROOKES

OAKWOOD PUBLISHING

This book is a work of non-fiction based on the author's experiences. In order to protect privacy, names, identifying factors, dialogue and details have been changed or reconstructed.

Published by OAKWOOD PUBLISHING
www.dawnbrookespublishing.com

Paperback Edition 2019
ISBN: 978-1-913065-02-7

Cover Design by Janet Dado

Contents

Preface

This is the third and final account of my years as a trainee nurse. I initially trained as a state enrolled nurse (SEN), meaning that it took me a lot longer to get to the stage where I was a registered general nurse (RGN). Had I known how long it would take, I would probably have opted for going straight into RGN training when the tutors realised from my first entrance exam that I had the ability to do this. On reflection, I'm pleased I didn't realise this, though, as I may well have stayed in Leicester for the rest of my career and missed out on London days that count among my favourite and happiest times.

With hindsight, I'm pleased my trainee years went the way they did and that I moved to the south of England, where I lived for the best part of thirty years, made many friends and trained as a cardio-thoracic specialist nurse, a RGN, a midwife and a district nurse, gaining two degrees along the way.

This book focuses on the details of a two-year conversion course I completed in a town in the south of England from 1982–1984, and my experiences of that course and the people I met. My enrolled nurse training and a little of my RGN training are covered in Book 1 of this series, *Hurry up Nurse: Memoirs of nurse training in the 1970s*. My cardio-thoracic course and how I managed to get an RGN training place is covered in Book 2, *Hurry up Nurse 2: London calling*.

Life as a trainee nurse before Project 2000 was gruelling, but also thrilling and fulfilling and I wouldn't have had it any other way. I'm grateful to friends, colleagues and patients who made the journey count among some of the best years of my life.

Dawn Brookes

The Plight of a First Year

Poem Sue Dundon

This poem was written by a friend and fellow nurse. It describes the lot of a junior nurse

I am a first-year student nurse
And I'm being socialised,
I have to work and work and work
Without it being realised.

The auxiliary is very helpful,
She tells me what to do.
She is very friendly with sister
And I hope I will be too.

But I'm not in sister's good books,
I gave a thirsty man a cup of tea.
I only found out later
He was fasting for an IVP.

The school of nursing didn't tell me

How hard I would have to work.
They tell you how to do some things,
But on the ward it doesn't work.

The whole of my set do get on very well
We go through heaven and hell,
We take our moans and groans back to the nurses'
home,
But we have lots of fun as well.

The home sister is a dragon
She won't give me a pass to go out,
But when I'm ill she's an absolute angel,
Of that there can be no doubt.

The medical staff don't talk to me
They make me like a wee moose.
When the Consultant comes to do his round
I disappear to the sluice.

Oh how I wish I was a third year
I might have better things to do,
I might even be able to talk to patients

Without getting myself in a stew.

The staff are always watching me
To make sure I'm working hard,
But I hope things will be different
When I'm eventually in charge.

Sue Dundon

First published in *Medicinal Verse,* edited by Kerrie Pateman, 1995

Chapter 1

Another Hospital, Another Town

What on earth was I doing pitching up at yet another school of nursing to take yet another course? Not only that, I had landed in yet another town. I had been nursing for five years, but here I was, doing all these things once more.

'Why should I train again?' I asked.

My Irish friends laughed at me. 'To be sure, to be sure!' they joked.

It was the first day of my shortened two-year training course to become an RGN at last. The course was referred to as a conversion as nurses converted from being enrolled nurses to registered nurses.

I woke early, grabbed a coffee, a slice of bread and butter, and left my new place of residence to see what life had in store for me over the next few years. It was a cold but bright September morning as I revved up the engine of my Suzuki 125 to ride to the hospital. I knew the way following a recce the day before. The roads were busy with traffic as it would be a rush hour – 9am – start, but thankfully I could skirt around most of the traffic on my newly acquired motorbike.

Once I arrived at the hospital, I parked up under a bike shed next to the school of nursing. *Surely they won't mind a motorbike being next to the row of bicycles?* I didn't have time to find out, instead heading towards the school of nursing building block in the hospital grounds.

Crowds of giggly girls milled around inside, and although I was only twenty-three myself, they seemed much younger. Either that or I felt older than my years. I was joining a set of second-year students for the shortened RGN training course. The school of nursing was relatively small, although not as small as the prefabricated unit I'd come to know and love at the London Chest Hospital – I sighed. How I missed London!

The main foyer area led into a larger hall with seats scattered about around small coffee tables. The walls had been plastered with magnolia coloured paint and were adorned with notice boards; no pictures, just notices and signs. The reception – if you could call it that – was manned by a woman in her fifties who looked like she'd dropped straight in from a library. Speaking of which, the library on the first floor of the building seemed to extend to places there just wasn't room for – a bit like Mary Poppins' bag! In reality, it stretched over a bridge leading to the doctors' boardrooms.

The racket from the excitable girls rang through the air. Their greetings, hugs and kisses surrounded me as they returned from their latest placements or holidays to begin their second year. I didn't know a soul and wondered if I'd be able to settle back into trainee life after the responsibility of being a specialist nurse in a hospital just a few months before. It was a good thing I'd taken a break.

I sighed again. 'You can do it,' I told myself while reassuring myself I would soon make friends. I always did.

Feeling more optimistic, I made my way to the reception, which was really just a window. I peered through the glass separating the receptionist from anyone approaching and preventing them from crossing into the hallowed land behind – a pretty small office, it has to be said.

The librarian lookalike came to the window and opened a small shutter.

'Yes?'

'Hello. My name's Dawn Brookes, I'm joining the September 1982 set today.' I smiled happily.

'Just a minute.' She leaned back and pulled out a list from a file, running her finger down it. Thankfully not too far – one of the advantages of having a surname beginning with B.

Her finger stopped. 'Yes, you are. Classroom 3 – over there, turn right.'

'Thanks,' I replied and crossed the room to where she had indicated. I made my way through yet more clusters of excitable girls – not one male nurse in sight – enjoying reunions. I found the classroom already half filled with nineteen to twenty-year-old girls; three older women, appearing to be in their forties, stood out among the group. Finding an empty desk, I sat down, plonking my crash helmet under the table. One of the older women seated nearby looked as bemused as I did.

'Hi,' I said. 'I'm Dawn, joining the set today.'

'Thank goodness,' she said, absently running a hand through her curly black hair. 'I thought I was the only one. Wendy, I'm Wendy. Are you doing the conversion, then?'

It always sounded like conversion should relate to a religious experience rather than a training programme and it made me smile. In spite of the fact that I had already done two years' SEN training, one year cardio-thoracic training, run wards and worked in intensive care units, this course would humiliatingly haul me back to square one. I had resigned myself to jumping through this hoop to get where I wanted to be, but didn't kid myself it would be easy. I wanted to be a registered nurse, and this was the only way.

I replied, 'Yes, I am. You?'

'Yes. It's odd being back in a classroom again – I trained years ago. They're all so young.' She laughed. 'I've been training some of these girls on the ward and now I'm one of them. Ironic, isn't it?'

'You're from this hospital then?'

'Yes, I've worked on women's surgical for the past fifteen years. Decided it was time to take the plunge and do the conversion now my children are a bit older. I'm fed up with training people who then become senior to me as soon as they qualify.'

I had a lot of sympathy for Wendy because that was the lot of the SEN. Some of them became bitter about the injustice of the way the system worked. Others seemed happy not to have as much responsibility and to be more hands-on, but what was unfair was that one day they were senior enough to run a ward, and the next day when a staff nurse – even if newly qualified –

came on duty, they would be treated like a student or worse. I hadn't had enough time to experience this frustration because I was still young and my feet had barely touched the ground after qualifying – I more or less moved straight down to London to undertake specialist training. I'd been so busy, but I am pretty sure if I'd stayed an enrolled nurse, I would have found it hard.

Enrolled nurse training never existed in the United States and no longer exists in the United Kingdom, and the qualification has been removed from the Nursing and Midwifery Council (NMC) register altogether. Enrolled nurses were given the option to convert in the 1990s through a much simpler process than the one I undertook; in fact, I was a tutor to many converting through a distance learning course in the late 1990s. Only a few enrolled nurses still remain who opted not to convert, biding their time until they can retire.

'Where have you moved from?' asked Wendy.

I explained how I'd been an enrolled nurse in Leicester, moved to London to do a cardio-thoracic course and worked at the London Chest

Hospital up until three months ago when a friend and I had decided to tour Asia before I moved here. As I looked around and heard a few of the girls sharing their holiday experiences of Benidorm or Bognor, I sat back and sighed yet again. I didn't know whether to be smug or culture shocked about my return to the United Kingdom.

Later that morning, I asked the tutor, Mrs Crisp, if I would get a tour of the hospital. She laughingly explained that tours were only given at the beginning of the first year.

'Don't worry,' she told me. 'You'll find your way around soon enough.'

By lunchtime I was restless and needed a walk and a cigarette. My on-off relationship with smoking was back on, so I thought I'd undertake my own tour. The school of nursing stood in the grounds off one of three entrances from a road that spanned the west side of the hospital. I decided to follow an inside path running parallel to it and leading through the hospital grounds up the hill towards the rear. On my walk, I passed gynaecology outpatients and dermatology. I also saw patients and visitors making their way in to one of the main corridors that led through the hospital.

Unlike when I first started training, we didn't have to wear uniform when in "block" (as classroom training was referred to), so I sat under a tree, smoking my cigarette. I stayed still for a while, studying my surroundings and observing worried faces and ill faces. I watched people coming and going and wondered what troubles they carried with them as they entered and left the hospital. If you stand still outside a hospital, or even in a corridor of a hospital, you will see a multitude of stories unfold in a matter of minutes. It doesn't take a detective to work out what's going on.

Each face told its own story: an elderly man sat on a bench staring into space, probably having received bad news judging by the tear that fell unbidden down his cheek. Was it his news or someone else's that caused him such pain? A woman in her forties came out of the gynaecological outpatients department sporting a huge grin on her face as she fell into the arms of another worried looking man standing outside. Obviously she had had good news.

Inside the hospital, staff bustled along the corridors, all heading to some unknown destination, oblivious to the fact I was watching on. I saw nurses walking alongside patients heading to X-ray or theatre; porters chatting to patients as they wheeled them along corridors; doctors with stethoscopes hanging around their necks like a new scarf; admin staff wearing suits with badges pinned to their lapels. Within half an hour, I'd discovered where the large Nightingale wards were situated – they ran along the front and sides of the hospital, where the maternity unit stood near the top of the road, and casualty at the rear of the hospital. A woman was being shouted at by a man – presumably her husband – as children followed, most likely being dragged along unwillingly to either visit sick relatives or accompany one of the parents to an appointment.

Casualty backed on to yet another road. The hospital was huge, probably on a par with the Leicester Royal Infirmary where I had spent a large part of my enrolled nurse training, and the main building and its grounds were surrounded by four different roads. The main entrance to the older part of the building had been erected on the London Road, but only people who took the bus entered the hospital that way as parking was limited. The school of nursing was closer to the front of the hospital, but you had to leave the main corridor to get out to it or enter via the road I'd come in on that morning.

I had sufficiently familiarised myself with the layout of the hospital by the time I made my way back to the classroom for an afternoon of lectures and giggly girls. These young women would be responsible for caring for some of the people I'd observed going in and out of the hospital; I wondered what kind of nurses they would be. I hoped they would be caring, like the ones I'd worked with in London. I hoped they would try to understand the fear that many of the people coming in and out of my new hospital would be experiencing and that they would take the time to communicate compassionately with them. One thing I did know was that if they hadn't grown up already during their first year, they would do so pretty fast over the next few years. Some young women in this room would go on to great things; others would leave, get married or get pregnant; a small minority would become automatons who didn't give a damn about the people in their care. I would find out who would be who all in good time.

I was right about making new friends. A few weeks later it was as though I'd been with this set right from the start.

Chapter 2

The Week Before: Homeless

It was all well and good doing a three-month trek round Asia, but now I was back in London, needing to move to a town forty miles away to start my RGN training next Monday. The small problem of where I was going to live occupied my mind as I dossed down on my friend Sheila's floor at the London Chest Hospital.

'Stay as long as you like,' Sheila had told me, but her real meaning was, *I know you have to be gone by the weekend so I'll put you up until then.*

It was great being back in London; I had thoroughly enjoyed the Asia trip, but there was no place like home – figuratively speaking, as the reality was I didn't have a home. The flight back from Karachi the day before had been a long one and I'd got the distinct impression that my travelling companion, Tina, was sick of the sight of me after three months living in each other's pockets. The fact that she hadn't offered to put me up in her flat spoke louder than words; it seemed she didn't care I might be homeless!

Travelling for that length of time with one person can be challenging, though, and I made allowances for that following her surprise outburst on the Tube on the way back from the airport. She had yelled at me over something particularly trivial and told me in no uncertain terms that I'd got on her nerves. I told myself, like Elizabeth Bennet in *Pride and Prejudice*, that it was good to have a short memory in such cases. I also reminded myself she was an only child and not used to sharing.

We parted ways with no real goodbye, both still a bit jetlagged. Years later, we did get back in touch with each other, after I'd moved away from London and Tina had married. We wrote to each other for many years, moving on to Facebook messaging in more recent times, both glad that our great adventure when we were young hadn't done irreparable damage to our friendship.

After Tina and I had gone our separate ways back in the early eighties, I decided to head back to Bethnal Green to see if anyone would let me stay overnight. I had been shocked by Tina's outburst, but I had bigger fish to fry as it was time to plan how to get to my new town and place of work. I only had a few days to work out where I might live.

Thankfully my old friends were only too pleased to see me on my return. I hadn't had the chance to get on their nerves for over three months, so they were happy to hear about my travels through Asia. My Australian friend, John, offered to put me up, but I thought staying with him in a tiny room and only a single bed might be challenging – for me, if not for him. We'd already been down that road before I left and it wasn't one I wanted to return to.

Sheila was on an early shift when I asked if I could stay an extra night while I sorted myself out, which was when she told me I could stay for as long as I liked. I heard her get up for work and climbed into her bed as soon as she left, exhausted and a bit jetlagged. I had heard that jetlag wasn't as bad going from east to west as it was going the opposite way, and so far that was proving true. Although I was still in a different time-zone, at least Karachi was only four hours ahead. Even so, I had been wide awake since 3am! It was difficult not making a noise in a room the size of a cardboard box, and to make matters worse, Sheila snored most of the night, but beggars couldn't be choosers.

I eventually got up at 10am after catching a bit of sleep, feeling ready for lunch. I found John in his room. He'd told me he had a few days off and wanted to hear all about my trip, particularly as I had stayed with one of his friends in Singapore. We spent some time catching up and I told him I really needed to sort out where to live before Monday. In typical horizontal Australian style, he reassured me it would work itself out.

'A bit like you telling your friend in Singapore we were coming to stay and us arriving with him not knowing who the heck we were sort of "work itself out", you mean?'

'He put you up, didn't he?'

I had to admit it had worked out, but with no thanks to John. At this moment, though, all I had in my hand was a letter with a start date for next Monday. The letter instructed me to arrive at the School of Nursing at 9am. Accommodation hadn't been an option for students undertaking an enrolled nurse conversion course – in fact, very little was offered to students undertaking the conversion course, if the sparse letter was anything to go by. Still, I was going to train as an RGN and that was all that mattered to me. I would be joining a group of students beginning their second year of training as my course had a year knocked off for good behaviour.

John couldn't believe the way the British system worked. 'Two years training as an enrolled nurse, two years working as a qualified nurse and one year training on a specialist course, and it counts for *one year*?'

'Yep, I'm afraid so, but it's only two years of my life.' Forever the optimist – no wonder I drove Tina mad on our travels.

I checked through my address book and decided there was nothing for it but to phone one of my ex-flatmates. She was married and living in a small village around fourteen miles from the town I would be working in, and she owed me big-time for the hours I'd spent painting flipping Artex all over their cottage walls before she and her husband moved in. If I'd known back then it contained asbestos, I wouldn't have been quite so keen to help.

The pips after I'd dialled from the phone box in the main hospital corridor told me it was time to put money in.

'Jess, hi.'

'Dawn, is that you? It's absolutely delightful to hear from you. Are you back in the United Kingdom?' My friend spoke with a plum in her mouth and lived by the philosophy: why use two words when you can use twenty? Still, it was a good start.

'Yes, got back yesterday.'

'I can't wait to hear all about your travels. Oh wait until I tell Brian and Mummy you're back. You must come and tell us all about it, everywhere you went and who you met.'

At this point in the conversation I was recalling the time Jess had gone away to the Cayman Islands, met a wealthy bachelor and broken off her engagement to Brian on her return home. Our friends and I had lived through every detail of the trip, from the daily temperatures to the colour of Bachelor Boy's socks; I felt I had been there myself by the time she'd finished. Thankfully she had got over the infatuation and married Brian who took her back with open arms, despite her infidelity.

I was hauled out of my reverie when she asked, 'When does your course start?'

'Monday.'

'That soon? Have you got anywhere to stay?'

'No, not yet.'

'Oh, you must come and stay with us until you find somewhere. Brian will be pleased to see you;

we have so much to catch up on. When can you come?'

I love you, I love you, I love you! 'Would tomorrow be alright?'

'Yes, of course. Are you getting a train? Brian can collect you if you let me know your arrival time.'

The telephone pips were now going demented so I put another coin in the phone.

'No, it's okay. I have a lift. Sorry, got to go, I don't have any more change. See you tomorrow, bye.'

Making my way back through the hospital corridor with a huge smile plastered on my face, I traipsed outside, through the courtyard that doubled up as a building site thanks to permanent renovations and a hospital extension that took longer to build than the Channel Tunnel, and upstairs to John's room, giving him the thumbs up.

'Will you be able to drive me to Jess and Brian's tomorrow? It's about forty miles.'

'No worries,' he answered in the Australian drawl that I had grown to love. 'What we gonna do today, then, mate?'

We decided to go into the West End as it might be a while before I could visit London again. I would be back to living on a student nurse's salary and was stony broke following the Asia trip. We went to all my favourite places, including *My Old Dutch*, a pancake house in Russell Square that I adored. That evening I caught up with some more of my friends and we went to the local pub, *The Bonner*, for a few drinks.

The next morning, I packed up my "worldly goods", squashing them into the one bag I possessed. I'd bought it in Thailand – a multi-pocketed dark blue holdall with tan leather decorations around all of the pockets. I no longer owned a camera, having sold mine in India to raise some much-needed funds. With mixed feelings, I said cheerio to the few friends that were on late shifts or days off and jumped into John's battered old car.

I hated leaving London. Having been so happy in the Capital, first living in the East End, then in a flat in Stoke Newington, I had wanted to stay there forever. If I'd already been a registered nurse, I knew I wouldn't be leaving, but I needed the RGN qualification as much as I needed air to breathe, so the deed had to be done. This was my only ticket, but I still choked back the tears as John started the car.

Jess came rushing out her front door as soon as John pulled the car up outside her house, a Victorian terrace about eight doors away from the village pub. I'm sure she and Brian had chosen the cottage based on its proximity to the pub as it took away all worries about drink-driving. It was before the days of mobile phones so she must have had telepathic senses, or been staring out the window.

Jess didn't know John at all, but having been brought up with a father ranking highly in the

RAF, she was used to making people feel at home. Having said that, she was also used to servants and a cook, but I didn't see any of those around. Within minutes, she had offered John overnight accommodation, which he gratefully accepted, along with a pot of tea. Pot, not mug; she was very British.

Jess and I caught up on each other's news while Brian took John out to see his Austin Bentley sports car – the same car he and Jess had driven away in for their honeymoon. After dinner, we all walked along to the village pub and spent a pleasant evening playing catch-up. John and Brian hit it off immediately; Brian was a few years older than me and Jess, but nowhere near as old as John, and there was no shortage of conversation.

Jess took me aside and asked if John and I were an item, so I explained that he had asked me out quite a few times before I went away, but there was a twenty-year age gap between us, not to mention there would now be a forty-mile distance, too.

'I like him, he would be great for you. So laid back.'

'I like him too, but it wouldn't work. I need to concentrate on my training over the next two years, and anyway, he's too old. When he's sixty, I'll only be forty.'

'Forever the pragmatist, Dawn. When are you going to fall in love?'

'Never, if I can help it. I don't want to give my love to just one person, I'd be claustrophobic.'

Jess would never understand my philosophy on love, but she did understand about the gruelling training I was about to undertake. She was already a state registered nurse (SRN) and registered sick children's nurse (RSCN) as she had trained for four years and obtained a joint adult and children's nurse qualification. We had met through a mutual friend when a group of trainee nurses were doing their adult placement in Leicester. She and my two other ex-flatmates had trained at Great Ormond Street, but we all went our separate ways after Jess and Brian married. Angie had stayed in London, but moved in with her boyfriend, and Jade moved back into the nurses' home.

We reminisced for a while about the old days after the pub had closed and finally went to bed at around two o'clock in the morning. Jess and Brian were working the next day, but had told me about the buses going into town.

'I think I'll need to buy a motorbike if I'm going to travel fourteen miles every day.' I was starting to worry about the distance because I hadn't passed my driving test and reality was sinking in. Before the Asia trip, my only experience of motorbikes had been as a pillion passenger, but Tina and I had hired bikes on numerous occasions while travelling in Thailand and learned on the job, a bit like nurse training.

'There's a bus every hour from across the road,' Jess assured me. Before going to bed, she and Brian said I could stay with them for as long as I wanted to.

I heard Jess and Brian get ready for work the next morning and waited until they left the house before rising. John had to get back to London and

I saw him off. He kissed me before leaving and said, 'You've got great mates there,' and then I was left alone in a strange village, not knowing how I was going to manage the commute while working hospital shifts. My situation might be manageable for a short time, but certainly not for long.

Before going to bed the previous night, I had prayed for three things: that I would find somewhere to live quickly; that I would find a motorbike shop the next day; and that I would find a church to settle into. Not much to ask, surely!

By the time John had left, I was very much up and dressed, ready to explore the town where I would be working. Crossing the road to the bus stop about ten minutes before the bus was due, I waited in silence. I knew a little bit about the small village Jess and Brian lived in from the times I'd stayed when we were doing up their cottage before they got married. It had typical village amenities, but I wasn't much interested in it as a place to live because it would be too far away from work.

The bus journey was straightforward enough, but took well over an hour due to regular stops on the way. It passed through several other villages, including Pangbourne where I noticed the weir that had inspired the author of *Wind in the Willows*. Jess had told me to look out for it the night before, and as the bus stopped right outside the pub where the weir was situated, I couldn't really miss the place where Ratty had made his friends.

By the time the bus arrived in town, it was after midday. I didn't know the town at all, and had no intention of staying there after my two years' training. How little we know of the future! I got off the bus on a main road, a stop before the town centre as it happened, and spotted a motorbike shop across the road as soon as the bus moved on. One prayer answered, my usual optimism returned.

I crossed over the road, smiling, and saw a small round man with messy red hair wearing greasy blue overalls, bending down fixing something on one of the many bikes in the shop. He stood up and smiled a friendly smile.

'Hello, what can I do for you?' It was fairly unusual in the 1980s to find young women going into a motorbike garage.

'I'm looking for a small motorbike suitable for a learner,' I answered. Back then you could ride a motorbike on a provisional licence for as long as you liked, as long as L plates were on display. The engine size was restricted to below 125 cc, though.

He looked a bit askance. 'Have you ridden a motorbike before?'

Typical bloke attitude, I thought, but answered confidently.

'I learned in Thailand.' I assured him that if I could ride amongst kamikaze Thai drivers, I would manage in this town. Then I explained how I had just returned from a journey around Asia and was staying with friends in a village fourteen miles away, but was due to start work at the main hospital on Monday.

He wiped greasy hands down his overalls and smiled again. 'You're in luck, then. Me and my wife have a basement flat for rent.'

I gawped. He explained that he and his wife knew the village where I was staying because they went to church there.

'It will be a difficult journey from there if you need to work shifts, but from our house it would take you five to ten minutes to get to the hospital on a motorbike, and twenty minutes to walk.'

I couldn't believe my luck!

The man left a young lad in charge of the garage and walked me the five minutes to his house. As we entered through the front door into a long hallway, the mess struck me, but it could have been a lot worse. I'd just returned from places where people lived on the streets and washed in puddles.

He called his wife downstairs. A woman in her early thirties with long, greasy dark-brown hair stepped over toys and clothes, randomly strewn across the hallway, to reach us. They invited me upstairs as it was one of those houses where the lounge was on the first floor. I followed them through the obstacle course to a lounge even more untidy and cluttered than the hallway. The man introduced himself as Graham and explained that his wife didn't like housework.

Understatement of the year! The place was more like a junkyard than a house; if I hadn't been there with the owners, I would have thought it had been burgled. Clothes, toys and remnants of food were scattered all over the place; the three scruffy children and one scruffy dog I would meet later. But needs must. I was thankful that in India I had shared rooms with lizards and giant cockroaches; otherwise I might have run for the door.

We drank tea, certainly not made in a pot, and I didn't pay too much attention to the mug for fear of what I might see. Having said all this, I don't want to sound derogatory. They were really nice people who went out of their way to welcome me, a stranger, into their home.

After a while, they escorted me back downstairs and unlocked a door in the hallway that led down some steps into the basement flat. The flat, or rather, bedsit didn't look too bad at all; a lot cleaner than the house upstairs. It was a bit musty and damp, but it had a bedsitting room fully equipped with a Baby Belling cooker, and a shower room with toilet. I think sharing the toilet with the messy family upstairs would have been more than I could take, even though I had come to grips with holes in the ground on the Asia trip!

We agreed I could move in at the weekend and I paid a deposit. I don't think there was ever a contract; it was a handshake agreement without the handshake as Graham's hands were too greasy. Then I went back to the garage with him and chose a dark blue Suzuki 125 that was around five years old and within my price range. He said he would service it for me and have it ready for Sunday when I moved in. He also sorted out some L plates and a helmet that would fit on my head. I couldn't have been more pleased and felt like a huge weight had been lifted from my shoulders. Stage one had gone so much better than I could ever have imagined.

After leaving Graham's garage, I walked into town and ate a late lunch. I looked around the shops, found a W H Smith where I bought a map, and then headed back to the main road to get a bus back to Jess's.

Jess and Brian were flabbergasted when I told them the story that night. Jess was disappointed that I wouldn't be staying longer, but understood it would be for the best.

John was coming back the next day for the weekend, and when I phoned him with the news, he said he would help move me on Sunday. Thankfully the flat was furnished because I didn't have much in the way of belongings.

John, Jess and Brian helped me to move into my new flat on Sunday morning. It was more a matter of them wanting to see where I was going to be living than helping, as I only had the one bag! Jess wasn't impressed with the hallway, and was even less impressed with the basement flat.

'It's damp and it smells musty. Are you sure you're going to be alright here? Who are these people? Don't they own a vacuum cleaner?'

I had to laugh. As she'd been brought up in a military household with a cook and cleaners, this was Jess's idea of hell. I doubt that one shred of dust had been allowed to remain in her family home, and her cottage was just as tidy.

'It's only until I find somewhere else and it saves me travelling the fourteen miles into town every day,' I answered reassuringly. John didn't look any less concerned than Jess, but he held his peace.

We went out for a pub lunch locally, and then Jess and Brian headed back home and John left for London. I was pleased when they all left because the tension had been building in Jess throughout the afternoon. I was beginning to think she might haul me into the car and take me back with her, or have me certified.

Graham and his wife, Sharon, had stayed out of the way while I moved in, which was perhaps as well. Although I could see the mess whenever I went upstairs, it wasn't *my* mess. As with so many things, I have no regrets with regards to my short tenancy in the basement flat.

Graham had given me the keys to the flat and the front door of the house when I arrived. I noticed my Suzuki parked on the front drive and found the key in an envelope by the kettle, along with the ownership documents that I had to complete. I had sorted out insurance the day before, finding a broker in the town centre that Graham had told me would give me a reasonably cheap policy as he used them all the time.

I decided first to take a walk to the hospital, using the map I had bought. The letter from the hospital gave the address of the School of Nursing and I knew I would remember the building once I got there from my interview earlier in the year.

The interview stood out in my mind. I'd taken a Tube from Bethnal Green to Paddington, and then a train followed by a bus journey to the hospital, but just as I was about to enter the building, the heel of my shoe had caught in a drain and come away. I was running out of time and couldn't do anything about it, so I shoved the heel in my handbag and tried to walk as if nothing was amiss. The trickiest bit had been following a secretary to the interview room and entering without giving the game away. I was grateful that on concluding the interview, the tutors had dismissed me and chatted to each other while I made my way out of the room cautiously, trying to walk as if I had two heels.

Once outside the building, I had walked uncomfortably into town and found a cobbler who told me they could glue the heel. I ended up walking in my stockinged feet into a café where I sat for an hour before collecting the mended shoe. Thankfully, a few weeks later I received a letter from the hospital offering me a place, otherwise I might have been tempted to post a broken shoe to the interviewer.

Now, I wanted to know how long it would take to walk to the hospital, and to see if there was anywhere to park my motorcycle once I decided to ride it in. Following the map, I took just over half an hour to get there with a bit of stopping and starting to check directions. I figured it would take twenty minutes at a fast pace; it was about a mile from where I was now living. Not bad at all. It could have been a lot further away, so I was thankful for my little basement bedsit for now.

I located the School of Nursing through a side gate leading into the hospital grounds. It wasn't a big building and was locked up, so I was unable to enter. I walked along the road inside the hospital and noticed a bicycle shed on the right-hand side which might do for parking my bike – there was already a moped parked up.

There was no long-term parking on the road outside – the sign read "Two hours parking Monday to Friday". Alongside the limited parking area stood an old building with one entrance, but multiple windows. It stretched for a couple of hundred yards and had to be a nurses' home – it just had that look about it.

Having completed my task for the day, I decided to amble back to my flat and get unpacked ready to start training the next day. The thought cheered me up because I was missing

London and didn't know anyone in this town, apart from the rather eccentric couple whose flat I was renting. There wasn't a phone in the flat and this was well before the days of mobile phones, so I felt isolated and alone with no outside contact. Graham had said I could use their phone upstairs, but I suspected that if I ventured up there, it might not be easy to escape again. And I was right – many a conversation lasted far longer than I would have liked when I did go upstairs during my tenancy. It wasn't that I didn't like them; I did, but the mess was unsettling. There was never anywhere to sit; food and drink spillages covering the floor stuck to my shoes – there was no way I was taking them off; and Sharon was always pleased to hand me the chubby six-month-old baby whose face was often dripping with something or other that ended up landing on my clothes. In spite of all of this, they were a happy family and the children didn't lack for anything (other than a wash).

But I digress.

I got back to the flat at around 6pm and unpacked the few clothes I had, hanging my one suit in the small wardrobe. The rest of the clothes I piled into a chest of drawers, and then I took in the details of the flat for the first time.

It was pretty dark as the only window was below street level. A Formica-topped table and two chairs sat in a tiny patch that constituted the dining section. In the main living area was a two-seater settee and a single bed. The kitchen had a few cupboards and one of those really old fridges that spent years destroying the ozone layer for future generations, but in my defence, I didn't know it at the time.

The walls were artexed, a fact I'd pointed out to Jess and Brian, knowing how much they loved the stuff and hoping to distract them from the musty smell, but to no avail. It was all painted white while the floor was covered with an old Axminster patterned castoff that must have come from the same roll that carpeted the upstairs lounge and stairs. It wasn't fitted; rather it had been plonked in the middle of the floor, and the frayed edges suggested it had seen better days.

This carpet also accounted for the musty smell from rising damp. As soon as I sat down, I could feel the damp – I already knew it was damp because of the dankness in the air, not to mention Jess pointing it out continuously before she'd left.

The window provided a view on to a concrete enclosure about eight feet below the level of the driveway. Light didn't really penetrate through the window, making it hard to tell whether it was day or night most of the time.

Everything seemed to stand still that evening. I was beginning to realise why John was worried about me staying in the flat and I missed my friends already, but I had to pull myself together. I told myself it was a roof over my head and I was starting a new job the next day, and Jess had put a pint of milk in the fridge earlier and supplied me with a loaf of bread, some butter and a jar of coffee, so all was good so far.

Chapter 3

Giving Blood – or Not

During the second week of our initial block, a crowd of trainees went across the road to give blood as the blood transfusion crew was in town. After giving consent, and being told that my blood would need to be tested for infectious diseases which I presumed meant hepatitis B, I was asked to sit on a bed.

AIDs had hit the world's radar, but there had only been a few cases and it was not yet recognised as the danger it would later become. Terence Higgins had died of the disease in the summer of 1982 while I was on my travels, but the significance of his death was not known at the time. The disease became much more prevalent over the next few years and the HIV virus was identified in 1986 – the year I started midwifery training, as it happens.

AIDs was initially thought to be a disease confined to promiscuous gay men and drug addicts, so was largely dismissed as a low risk for the general population. Unfortunately, it didn't get the necessary attention until it became recognised as a heterosexual disease as well and after the first cases of contamination through infected blood were highlighted. In 1982 blood donors were not tested for the disease when giving blood and health professionals had no idea of the risks to them of this and other contaminants that were to arise from needle-stick injuries. Such injuries were extremely common for nurses – I had numerous during my nursing career – as we were still being taught to re-sheath needles after use before discarding them into a sharps container.

Not only were we in constant danger from infectious diseases, but the reporting of injury was appalling and generally not encouraged, so busy nurses and doctors just carried on with their work, hoping the cross-contaminated patient did not have hepatitis B. Later we discovered there were many more deadly contaminants, including HIV and hepatitis C.

Once the needle had been inserted in to my arm and the line attached, the nurse began the process of withdrawing blood and I felt all the life draining from my body.

'Am I supposed to feel as weak as this?' I asked as my legs and chest became heavy.

Without looking at me, the nurse answered, 'Don't worry, you'll be fine,' and carried on withdrawing blood.

'My limbs feel really heavy,' I said. I could tell that something was not right as I was beginning to feel like I was sinking away.

Finally she looked at me, and suddenly a crowd of people was around the bed as she disconnected the line. She tilted the foot of the bed up to bring my head down and I felt someone mopping my brow with a cold flannel.

'Did you eat before you came over?'

'No, I came straight from lectures.'

A cup of tea and a biscuit later, followed by a lecture on the need to eat and drink before giving blood and a lot of ribbing from my newfound friends, I was feeling normal again.

'At least we can send your blood off to test your suitability to donate,' the nurse said.

A few weeks later I got the all clear letter informing me that I could give blood anytime and that my blood group was O positive. Have I ever given blood since? Not likely!

Chapter 4

Operation Theatre

Looking forward to getting back to where the action was, I woke up excited and jumped on the motorbike, revving up the engine. It purred into life with the same degree of excitement I was feeling, and I arrived at the hospital in plenty of time for my 8am start in theatre. In fact, I arrived a bit too early and had time to kill.

After doing a few laps around the hospital grounds at a pace any motorbike lover would be proud of, I parked my trusty steed under the forbidden bike shed near to the School of Nursing. I had come to an agreement with the head porter that he wouldn't tell anyone I parked there if I didn't let on he knew about it.

I made my way towards the hospital theatres. Anticipating new levels of responsibility, with visions of major operations taking place and surgeons thanking me for my expert assistance at the end of each shift, I knocked on the door to theatre. No reply – not a good start. I didn't dare walk through the doors into theatre from the anaesthetic room because everywhere would be deemed sterile and I was still in my jeans and t-shirt, holding a crash helmet under my arm, so I waited for what seemed like an eternity until someone came along the corridor.

'What are you doing there?' he yelled.

'I'm Dawn Brookes, student nurse. It's my first day, I was told to report to theatre at 8am.'

'You need the changing room entrance, back there.' He nodded his head towards a corridor on the left.

'Thanks,' I said and trundled off, feeling like an idiot already. 'Great start, Dawn,' I muttered to myself.

I found a door clearly labelled THEATRE STAFF ONLY and pushed it open slightly. A woman dressed in a navy blue uniform, obviously the theatre sister, saw me.

'Yes?'

'I'm student nurse Brookes reporting for duty, Sister.'

She smiled a genuine smile. One had to learn the difference between sisters' smiles; some reached their eyes, and others warned, *I'm going to eat you up and spit you out.* It paid to do your homework – it was a matter of survival. This woman wore the good type of smile and I immediately relaxed.

'Well, come on in, then. We don't bite.' She sounded harsh, but there was a jolly tone to her voice which was not at all frightening. I had met many ogre sisters before and immediately sussed she was not one of them, although she did do a double take at the sight of my crash helmet.

'You be careful you don't end up in here on the other side,' she warned.

'I'll try not to.' I didn't know whether to laugh or not, so held my peace.

'Right, follow me.'

She led me into a large room lined with rows of tall, narrow metal lockers. Some had keys to demonstrate they were not in use; others had labels on them and were clearly locked.

'Change into a pair of those.' She pointed to a pile of scrub suits on a trolley. 'And put some clogs on. What size are you?'

Not sure if she meant clothes or feet, I answered for both. 'Size 10 dress and shoe size 5.'

She chuckled. 'You nurses get smaller and smaller.' Looking at her size 22 frame and six-foot stature, I could see where she was coming from. She towered over me in every way. 'Clogs are over there. Once you've changed, join us in the office through that door.'

'Yes, Sister.'

I had to stifle a "yippee" as I looked at the blue scrubs I was about to put on. I'd only been in theatre twice when working at the London Chest Hospital, once to watch a coronary artery bypass operation where I bumped heads with a theatre nurse who was none too pleased, and once when I was ensconced firmly behind a screen at the

Brompton Hospital to observe paediatric heart surgery. This would be the first time I got to see things working close up and personal.

The scrubs fitted, apart from the trousers; they were too long so I had to switch to a dress instead. Trousers were always too long for me – they came in one length to fit the average height woman and I was five foot nothing. One thing I always carried around was a sewing kit in case I needed to turn something up, but I was happy to wear a scrub dress as my uniforms were all dresses anyway. I only ever wore dresses at work and to weddings; otherwise it was skirts or trousers that had been turned up to fit.

I found a pair of white clogs with heavy cork bottoms on a bench that was lined with at least thirty pairs in various sizes. On another bench I saw the white boots that surgeons wore. There were male and female changing rooms – thankfully, as they were very much open for all to see with no private cubicles or anything of that nature. Female consultant surgeons were a rarity, but there was one female gynaecologist, and as time went by there were more and more female registrars and house officers who would scrub up to assist with surgery or, in the case of registrars, carry out surgery themselves.

I found the office easily enough and was pleasantly surprised to find the day started with a cup of tea in Sister's office. This was something I can honestly say I'd never encountered in a hospital before. Sister Blenheim hadn't introduced herself, but I'd spotted her name from a surreptitious glance at the badge above her voluptuous right breast. The badge appeared to be seated on a large shelf, but it didn't pay to stare at nurses' badges unless you were a lecherous old man or an over-eager doctor! The badges were always placed above a breast on women, but some nurses placed them over the nipple. Whether by design or naivety, I never knew, but it could be embarrassing when you needed to know their name.

Sister hauled me back from my musings and told me to study an A4 sheet of paper attached to a clipboard hanging on the wall. It consisted of three theatre lists for the day, and it was jam-packed.

The other nurses on duty introduced themselves. There were six staff nurses and three student nurses on shift.

'Theatre operating times run from 9–5, Monday to Friday, for planned surgery. We have to fit emergencies in where we can and out of hours, but you won't be expected to work any late shifts or weekends unless you want to volunteer as an observer,' Sister explained before whispering conspiratorially, 'I wouldn't if I were you.' I felt a little disappointed, but thought it would be nice to have a few weekends and evenings off for a change, having already spent most of my adult life working shifts.

Just when I was feeling happy and jolly, my luck changed. I was allocated a rather fierce-looking staff nurse to work with.

'Staff Nurse Wright will show you around. You can work with her today,' Sister informed me. I smiled over at the staff nurse in question but she looked away, rolling her eyes in the process. I got it – not every nurse liked having students following them around, but to be fair, in those days, students didn't do much following; they did most of the work.

Staff Nurse Wright was around forty, I guessed, and rake-like with cropped dark-brown hair that did nothing for her dour face, other than to make it look even more sullen than it already was. She wore horn-rimmed glasses and no wedding ring.

What did I do to deserve you? I could imagine her thinking this, because I was thinking exactly the same thing. All the other nurses were laughing and joking, talking about their weekends and boyfriends, and I was stuck with Sourpuss!

Shortly afterwards, SN Wright, aka "Chirpy", got up and left the office. I wasn't sure whether I should follow or not as she could have been going to the toilet for all I knew! One of the staff nurses smiled at me sympathetically and nodded towards the door, so I followed after my new leader like a puppy dog that had been kicked.

'We need to get Theatre 1 ready for surgery. Fill that up.' Chirpy pointed to a bowl in the sluice area where she had led me after handing me a theatre hat to cover my hair. The sluice was adjacent to the theatre and was where the surgeons and scrub nurses got ready before operating. I obediently filled a bowl with hot water and Chirpy added disinfectant. We then spent the next forty minutes washing everything – and I mean everything, despite the theatres having been cleaned at the end of surgery the night before. Who knew what dangerous microbes had marauded in the middle of the night? I began to visualise bacteria dancing around to disco music, having a theatre party after hours, and wondered if I would make a good cartoonist.

'Sister Blenheim,' I was informed by Chirpy, 'Will not tolerate any postoperative infections on her watch.'

My new leader, Sister Blenheim, was meticulous in every way, and so too were her staff. One thing I learned from hospital life was that a ward or, in this instance, theatre was only as good as the sister in charge – something modern-day hospitals could do with reflecting upon.

'Sister won't allow doctors or nurses to shortcut the rigid scrub-up times and no-one would dare to try,' one of the friendlier staff nurses told me later that day. 'Even the consultants who are bombastic demi-gods obey her rules of cleanliness and warn the junior doctors to do the same.'

After we had washed the theatre bed, all of the metalwork underneath, the theatre stools, anaesthetic trolleys, scrub trolleys, resuscitation equipment and the walls – yes, you heard right, the walls – the theatre was ready for the day. Just in time as we heard the first patient arriving in the anaesthetic room next door to the theatre. Two surgeons entered the sluice room through a different entrance, wearing white wellington boots and blue scrubs. They always looked strange in their *Ena Sharples* hats, but needs must.

Another staff nurse came through – I only knew who she was from her badge as everyone wore the same blue scrubs, which made identification difficult. I would be spending a lot of time checking badges as it was really hard to tell who was who once masks and hats were on, and I became very familiar with staff members' eyes when working in theatre. The eyes could tell me a lot about the person underneath the scrubs.

With an unnecessarily huge sigh, Chirpy pulled out a white theatre pack from a pile in a cupboard and placed it on the trolley in the main theatre.

'First op's a gall bladder,' she muttered.

Happy in your work, I thought sarcastically. This was going to be a long day if she didn't brighten up.

'Here, put this on.' She handed me a mask. It was even harder to recognise anyone now as everyone was wearing them, but Chirpy was easily identifiable due to her scowling green eyes and the lines on her forehead, not to mention her waiflike frame.

I peeped around the open doorway from theatre to the scrub room to see the doctors cleaning their fingernails and hands vigorously with a nailbrush and iodine. They washed and scrubbed to the elbows before drying themselves again. Chirpy pushed past me as though she were late catching a train as they donned their sterile green theatre gowns.

'You take that one,' she ordered. I had no idea what I was meant to do, but saw her tying up the gown at the back while the surgeon pulled on sterile gloves, so I did the same for the junior doctor and the scrub nurse. Chirpy only had time for the surgeon; all others were beneath her, it seemed, as she cold-shouldered them while oozing obeisance to the main man.

Once in theatre, everyone except for Chirpy carried on chatting as if nothing was happening, and I was pleased that I'd managed even this small task in spite of her. During surgery, everything in front of the surgeon and scrub nurse must be kept sterile, so they can only be approached from behind. In any other occupation that would just be plain rude, but woe betide a nurse who accidentally touched a gown in the wrong place. It was a frequent novice mistake; surgical registrars would laugh it off on the whole, but consultants often wiped the floor with the poor student nurse, taking great pleasure in doing so. The bigger the audience, the louder the dressing down. Unfortunately, surgeons were renowned for thinking too highly of themselves.

For the most part, the reputation was well deserved back in the day as they walked around followed by an entourage of junior doctors, rarely acknowledging the existence of patients or junior nurses. There were always the exceptions to the rule, and I did meet some surgeons who would smile and explain to a patient what the operation would involve, although I have to say that this didn't always go down well with the patient. Many preferred to be kept in the dark to revere the all-knowing surgeon; they didn't particularly want to be told he was going to amputate their leg or remove half their gut as if it was as easy as swatting a fly or buying a bag of chips.

There was no doubting the skill with which surgeons operated while talking about golf with the anaesthetist, who was equally blasé about it all. At the end of the day, routine surgery is just that, and most surgeons could do it with their eyes shut. The only fun some of them seemed to have was when someone dropped something so they could shout at them or if a junior doctor couldn't answer a question. Occasionally the scrub nurse would hand over the wrong instrument, which was almost a capital offense.

Nevertheless, it was all new to me and I watched operation after operation with wide-eyed enthusiasm, soaking the experience up like a sponge deprived of water. As I watched the surgeon hold out his left hand and the scrub nurse place an instrument into it without him even telling her what he needed, I soon realised that if that scrub nurse were to be in a village somewhere in the outback, she would be able to perform the same operation with almost the level of skill as the surgeons I observed. A sobering thought.

I say "he" for surgeon because the truth is that the majority were men; I didn't meet the female gynae surgeon until the mid-1980s, when they were still a rarity. Male nurses were becoming less rare, but I didn't come across any working in theatre. They tended to gravitate towards casualty or charge nurse positions, and men were much more likely to be promoted in spite of the nursing profession being female dominated across the board. There were, and still are, a disproportionately large number of men promoted to management throughout the NHS.

Although surgeons performed intricate operations with great skill while discussing golf and the price of whisky, if something went wrong, they would respond with speed and adept professionalism. During surgery, the surgeon would toss instruments and swabs backwards and forwards while the scrub nurse made sure instruments were placed meticulously to one side while the blood-soaked swabs were passed to assistants – in this first case, me and Chirpy – who would separate and lay them out on a towel on the floor to be counted later. After the surgeon had finished his operation, he would stop while the theatre went silent. The scrub nurse would count out the used and unused swabs to ensure all were present, and then she would do the same with the instruments.

'Ready to close,' she would say, and then conversation would resume as either the surgeon or his assistant (more often than not) would close the patient up again. The reason for this is obvious: no-one wanted to leave anything inside the patient that shouldn't be there.

I found the whole theatre thing fascinating, but my mum's dream of me locking eyes with a surgeon during an operation and the happy-ever-after ending never took place. But it wasn't unusual for a theatre sister and a surgeon to marry – or not. Some surgeons and/or theatre sisters got involved in extra-marital "open secret" affairs while others were fly by nights, but there were some happy marriages that began in theatres and, indeed, in hospitals in general. Nowhere near as many as portrayed in soap operas, though.

On my first day in theatre, I saw numerous bodily organs removed or exposed, and Chirpy had to nudge me a few times to get me to do some menial task – usually just when things were getting interesting. I did as I was told and thoroughly enjoyed my first day regardless. In between operations, all hell broke loose as we had to frantically clean and scrub again before the next operation while the surgeon went for coffee and the junior doctor wrote up the notes. If you ask me what I remember most about theatre, I would have to say cleaning! But that doesn't mean I didn't learn a lot.

It was during the third week of this placement that I was in orthopaedic theatre to witness an above-knee leg amputation. Orthopaedic theatre, I had been told, was like working on a building site as there was always the banging and clattering of tools and much of the operating equipment resembled a builder's toolbox, albeit a surgically sterile one. There were hammers, screwdrivers, chisels, files, but I would see even worse instruments/tools on this particular morning.

There is no way to describe an amputation other than barbaric. Thankfully, the patient was in a deep anaesthetic-induced sleep and had no idea what was going on. The orthopaedic surgeon looked at his trolley and examined various instruments that wouldn't look out of place in a torture chamber. When I say instruments, I mean saws. I have never watched horror movies that involve the use of saws because I have witnessed the real thing – except the patient generally survived, in my experience.

After the patient's skin and muscle was cut open, the surgeon selected a saw appropriate for the job in hand. I was the poor unfortunate who had to hold the leg up while he sawed through the bone, bringing forth a sound that is unlike anything else. Once I'd heard this unique sound, I'd remember it forever. The bed was high because the surgeon was tall, but I am small, and was trying to hold the dead weight of a man's leg at a forty-five degree angle.

The scrub nurse could see I was struggling. 'Rest it on your shoulder,' she suggested. Thankfully that worked, except that I now had a clear view of what was happening. As blood and bone spurted everywhere, I ended up looking like an extra in one of the horror movies I never watch. The assistant worked quickly to cauterise blood vessels, but not fast enough in my opinion, while the surgeon applied clamps that the scrub nurse handed to him. Thankfully, I was wearing the mask because an artery clamp came loose and I got showered before the surgeon managed to put his saw down and cauterise the bleed, applying another clamp. I almost dropped the leg, which would not have been good as it was only half off!

Deep breaths, I kept telling myself as I felt myself getting weaker. The leg belonged to a twenty-four stone diabetic man and there had been a lot of flesh to cut through before starting on the bone; even the surgeon was sweating.

At least he's getting his brow mopped, which is more than I can say for me, I thought.

Eventually the surgeon managed to cut through the bone and tossed the leg at me.

'Get that out of my sight,' he said as he rested, breathless, for a moment before starting repairs. I, on the other hand, reeled backwards under the weight of the leg and was about to end up on the floor, but was saved by – would you believe it? – Chirpy! She caught me and the leg in one swift movement and helped me dispose of it in a bag that would go to the incinerator.

She motioned me towards the sluice, and then, to my amazement, burst out laughing. We laughed and laughed until tears streamed down our faces. I think my tears were more of relief than anything.

Chirpy told me to go and take a shower and change my scrubs as I looked like a murderer. When I got to the changing rooms and saw myself in the mirror, I could see what she meant. I was covered in blood and I reeked.

Pleased I wasn't the squeamish girl who almost fainted on her first ward, I showered, changed and went back for more. Needless to say, Chirpy and I became firm friends after this incident and I grew to like her, even though she remained dour-faced most of the time. We had shared a moment, and those moments are all important within the stresses and strains of a nurse's life.

I was pleased to end my stint in theatres, not because it was boring or I was sick of cleaning – even though I was, but because I missed speaking with patients. In theatre, they were out for the count, or when I worked in recovery, they were too groggy to have a conversation with. I admired the surgeons and put up with their quirks, and I appreciated the skills the scrub nurses had developed, but I hadn't spoken to a patient for eight weeks solid and that just wasn't for me.

It was time to go.

Chapter 5

Women's Bits

Female gynaecology was an early placement for me at the largest of the town's three hospitals. I had lived in the town for two and a half weeks, with two of those spent in school (block). At twenty-three, I was feeling much older than my years – it was the Asia effect, I told myself. You couldn't spend three months travelling Asia and not be changed, and I was still finding it hard to adjust to life in affluent England. Not that I was affluent at all – stony broke, actually, but that paled in comparison to whole families I had witnessed living on the streets in India and washing in puddles. I had seen a man dying on the edge of a busy road in Madras, which had to be one of the hardest things I had ever come across and remains forever etched in my memory.

By the end of the block, I had got to know quite a few of the girls in my set and found they were inclusive and fun to be around. Now it was time to get back to ward work.

Bridget was admitted to the gynae ward following a miscarriage. She was thirty-three, married with two young boys aged under five, and had been expecting the couple's third child when pains started in the night. Sadly, at sixteen weeks, she lost the baby and needed a dilatation and curettage (D&C) to scrape away any remains and prevent infection.

I knew immediately I met her that she was a Christian – I like to think it was a sixth sense, but perhaps the Bible on the side of her locker gave it away. It turned out Bridget was married to a church elder of a non-denominational fellowship in a suburb of the town. That was the new church sorted out for me, then! Bridget and her husband, Aled, became friends, and I'm pleased to say that the following year, Bridget did give birth to her third child, a daughter.

Gynaecology often created conundrums for us nurses because young (and older) women were admitted to the ward for a termination of pregnancy and could be given a bed next to women who were desperately upset following a miscarriage or who had been admitted for fertility treatment. All in all, it wasn't a satisfactory situation, and we did our best to separate people, but it was not always possible. The old Nightingale wards were often heaving and the turnover was high.

There were times when two women would get talking and both would end up upset. One can't underestimate the guilt that many women felt when undergoing a termination of pregnancy, and if they found out they were next to someone who was upset at losing a baby, their guilt could be multiplied. And vice versa, when a woman had just lost a baby, she didn't always understand why someone would want to terminate a pregnancy. Yes, there were some women who seemed to use termination as a form of contraception and one couldn't help but feel impatient with these, but they were in the minority. The majority were not in that situation and it was never my place to judge.

I am human, though, and I couldn't help feeling that some women were being pushed into aborting their babies rather than offered support to continue with a pregnancy. Pressure could come from anywhere: partners who didn't want children yet, parents of young girls, friends and occasionally counsellors who should have known better. Women who had doubts were the ones who struggled the most with guilt and passing judgement on them, as many anti-abortion lobbyists would do, was just not helpful.

Greta was one such woman, filled with guilt. She had been admitted for bed rest due to a small bleed and what we called a "threatened abortion", or threatened miscarriage. I found her in tears during the afternoon.

'Can I get you anything?' I asked.

She continued to cry, and then looked up at me.

'It's my fault.'

I knew immediately what she was talking about; I had read her medical history and seen she'd had a vaginal termination of pregnancy (VTOP) six years prior to admission.

'You can't think like that.'

'I'm being punished. I knew it wasn't right, but I went ahead and had an abortion anyway. They told me at the pregnancy advice clinic I was too young and would regret having a baby for the rest of my life if I went through with it. They convinced me I should go for an abortion.'

I couldn't believe what I was hearing; the advisory clinics were supposed to be impartial and, as far as I was aware, they were meant to support girls and women to make up their own minds, discussing the pros and cons of childbirth. Perhaps she was mistaken or even making it up so she could blame someone else, although she appeared sincere.

'I went for a pregnancy test and was a bit taken aback when told that I was pregnant. The woman who gave me the result was cold and heartless.

She scorned me and I'll never forget her words: "What did you expect if you have sex without contraception?" She was right, but you don't always think logically, do you?

'The next thing I knew, I was receiving counselling for a termination. I told them I would prefer to keep the baby, but they said I was just feeling that way out of some misguided sense of doing the right thing. "Catholic guilt", they called it. They said I was too young and wouldn't make a good mother at my age; they told me I would be throwing my life away. I was only nineteen, but one thing they didn't tell me was that I was throwing someone else's life away: my child's. And now I'll never be able to have children. They didn't even give me the option to have the baby adopted, something I would have seriously considered.'

Greta sobbed some more.

This was a very thought-provoking conversation and one that I remembered for a long time afterwards. Thankfully Greta's pregnancy did continue and she was discharged looking much happier than when she had been admitted. I trust she went on to have a family and that her feelings of guilt were assuaged as a result.

Don't get me wrong, not all women showed such remorse, and some treated abortion as if they were returning an unwanted item to the shop. The majority were somewhere in the middle: rational women who, for their own personal reasons, decided pregnancy was not right for them.

Full disclosure here: I was a conscientious objector, which meant that I wouldn't be in theatre for a termination of pregnancy, but it didn't mean that I didn't understand why some women/girls made this difficult decision or that I felt I was any better than them. It just meant that I could not, in all good conscience, take part in the actual termination procedure, but I still had a duty of care to the patient. Unfortunately, some of my colleagues were more judgemental towards me than I ever would have been towards the people in my care. Like many workplaces, the sad truth is that the NHS could have an underlying culture of bullying, and being a conscientious objector could sometimes be enough to kick start a bullying mentality from other nurses.

'Nobody likes these do-gooder, holier-than-thou sorts, Dawn,' my colleagues would sneer. Bizarrely, I suffered for my choice more as a midwife than as a general nurse. I tried to explain my position, but some colleagues didn't want to know, so I found it was best not discussed. Life's complicated at times.

Phyllis was admitted for surgery following a diagnosis of leucoplakia of the vulva. A forty-nine-year-old Irishwoman, she was to have a total vulvectomy. If you don't know what a total vulvectomy is, be thankful because it means all your bits are intact.

Basically the whole vulva, including the clitoris, is removed and a woman is left with a urethra to wee out of and a hole for the vagina. Yes, you got it – female circumcision of sorts, only in Phyllis's case it was to prevent the spread of a very dangerous pre-malignant condition.

Phyllis took it in her stride, not at all concerned. She shared a house with a male friend and – not that it was any of my business – she maintained there was no sexual relationship and refused pre- and post-operative counselling. Gordon was a lovely, big teddy bear of a man with long beard and moustache, and their relationship appeared to be a full partnership without the sex. It worked for them. He visited every day and they chatted and laughed away the hours, both pre- and post-surgery.

'Not every relationship is about sex,' she assured me and I had to agree that in their case, it seemed to be true.

Phyllis and I became friends and I was frequently invited along to their house for dinner – maybe the only decent meal I ate in a month as takeaways and hospital food were my lot in life. Just in case you're wondering – their home was a one-bedroom bungalow. I'm only saying! Some people do sleep together for companionship, or it may have been good old Catholic guilt that prevented her from admitting to living with a man outside of marriage. They were of the older generation and, despite the sixties sexual revolution, not everyone was happy discussing sex openly. On the other hand, they could have been telling the truth – as I said, not really any of my business.

Gardinia had to be the most eccentric person I ever met, and as for her mother – words fail me! If ever women could talk, and I mean talk, these two would win any verbal diarrhoea competition. They didn't just talk, though; it was all politics mixed with New Age evangelism.

Gardinia was admitted for a hysterectomy as she had fibroids, and she happened to be in the bed next to Phyllis and a lovely thirty-three-year-old woman called Sharon. Sharon had three young children and a doting husband, but had tragically been diagnosed with metastatic ovarian cancer; she wouldn't live for more than a few months. If ever I have met an inspirational woman who knew how to laugh and joke in the face of adversity, Sharon would always have my vote.

The three women were total opposites in terms of upbringing, life and work, but they did what opposites often do – they got on like a house on fire. My life was all the brighter for getting to know them and we laughed the days away.

Gardinia and her mother were on a personal mission to free Nelson Mandela, a man I had never heard of who, they told me, happened to be locked away in a prison in South Africa. The first time I met Gardinia, it was to fill out her admission paperwork. I have no idea how asking someone for a few personal details can lead to: 'This man must be freed. We went to a march last week – look, here's a poster.' I had stared blankly at the picture, certain that I had only asked her if she was taking any medication at present. Perhaps whatever she was taking was hallucinogenic or psychotropic. I hadn't the foggiest what she was talking about, and talk about it she did.

To be honest, I couldn't bear to hear poor Nelson's name until much later in life when I realised he truly was a man fighting injustice. I still don't believe that fighting for a cause justified the ear-bashing this poor nurse received every time she met Gardinia and her mother.

In between the Mandela thing and the New Age homoeopathy, another thing they had going on, I could see clearly why neither Gardinia nor her mother had ever married. Not quite sure how her mother got pregnant, but there was never any mention of a father. Phyllis teased Gardinia mercilessly, which she took in good humour, and Sharon bantered away too once she was on the mend following major surgery.

I kept in touch with all three women after they were discharged from the ward, even meeting up with Gardinia and her mother at their large home in a small village in Buckinghamshire. Large it may have been, but it represented everything they stood for – cluttered, messy, disorganised, hippy but homely, and of course Gardinia drank black coffee while her mum drank herbal tea.

Sharon died six months after being discharged and we all attended the funeral at the request of her husband – a sad affair that has left a permanent cloud over my otherwise fond memories of female gynaecology.

Chapter 6

In the Sticks

My community placement was out in the country, twenty miles from the nearest town. It was a good job I had a car by then, not that the powers that be would have cared either way; I would just have had to make my way there via a rural bus route.

I was given the placement address at the end of a training block on the Friday before I was due to start and told to arrive at a place called The Quarry Health Centre at nine o'clock on Monday morning. I left early, not knowing what the traffic would be like, and with there being no satnavs back in the day, I used a map for guidance.

I arrived at a ramshackle old building on the outskirts of what was supposed to be a small town, but I would argue was more like a large village. It took me a while to find the entrance to the health centre as it really was not obvious. I walked around the red-bricked building a few times, searching for an entrance, but found that every door was locked.

Just as I was about to give up, I saw a woman who looked to be in her early 60s wearing a light blue staff nurse's uniform.

'Are you the new girl?' she asked.

'Yes, I am. I can't seem to find my way in and I think I might be late now.'

'Don't worry about that, follow me,' she said kindly.

I followed her round the corner to where there was a hidden door. I say it was hidden because it was just a large plank of wood, painted brown and nestling into the brick building. She entered a code into a large metal security lock on the outside, which was obscured by black plastic, hence my not having noticed it before. Even if I had noticed it, I wouldn't have known the code, and as there was no buzzer, I wouldn't have been any wiser. It screamed, "Visitors not welcome!"

Once inside the building, I followed her up a flight of stairs and soon heard laughter and talking in the distance. She pulled open a large, heavy door and we entered a huge room with around ten medium-sized wooden desks where four groups of people huddled. I followed my guide as we headed to the far right-hand corner.

'Look what I found hanging about outside,' the kind staff nurse said, chuckling.

'Hello, you must be Dawn,' said a woman who appeared to be in her late 40s. She wore a navy blue uniform and I rightly assumed she was the district nursing sister. I was a little taken aback because it was the first time I'd been called Dawn since starting my RGN training, other than by other student nurses. Most qualified staff still referred to me as Nurse Brookes.

She smiled and gestured for me to take a seat next to her by tapping the chair.

'Would you like a coffee?' she asked. I knew from that moment I was going to like community nursing. Never did you arrive on a hospital ward to be offered coffee. It was always a quick handover and off you went to work. This team appeared happy in their work.

That morning, there were three staff nurses, the sister who introduced herself as Jenny, and an enrolled nurse wearing a green uniform. There was also another student I hadn't met before; she certainly wasn't from my set and the stripes on her hat told me she was a second year. The hats were good identifiers as first years had one stripe, second years two, and third years three. Qualified staff wore frilly linen hats. I was now a third-year, so proudly wore the three light-blue stripes on my cardboard hat.

Initially the conversation revolved around who had done what the previous evening before moving on to talking about children, grandchildren and pets. Noticing my bemusement, Jenny laughed.

'Don't you worry, we work just as hard as they do in the hospital, but we don't make out we're God's gift. Right, on to business then,' she said and everyone quietened down.

She pulled an A4 book towards herself and opened it up. I noticed there were columned lists with the names of each nurse present at the meeting written at the top of the columns. Patients they would be expected to visit that day were listed below, and I saw from the length of the lists that it wasn't going to be all tea and coffee! Each nurse had around 12 to 15 patients to see, with the majority of them needing to be seen by lunchtime. After that, I was told we would meet up again to share around any other visits that came in during the morning.

The sister, Jenny, carried a bleep and it didn't take long for me to realise that this would go off constantly all day long. She would then have to find a telephone to discover who was calling her and why. I was allocated to work with Jenny that day, although I would be working with the other nurses in the team throughout my placement, which would last six weeks.

Jenny gave me a quick tour of the facility, for what it was worth. Basically, the building consisted of the large room and a storeroom on the ground floor. Although it was called a health centre, patients were not seen on site; it was a satellite office housing healthcare staff. She explained there were four teams based in the office we were in, each assigned to different GP practices.

Rows of large grey metal filing cabinets lined the outer edges of the office, containing district nurses' patient records. This was long before the days of computers on every desk. The desks were rather cluttered with diaries, documents and letters overflowing from in-trays, though.

On Jenny's desk there was both an in-tray and an out-tray, each filled with sheets of paper and envelopes. The nurses on duty had grabbed their diaries and were frantically writing down their work for the day, along with the addresses of patients who were new to them.

After the tour, Jenny picked up her own diary and indicated it was time for us to go. I proudly donned my navy blue outdoor raincoat and navy blue hat, standard issue for district nursing; I had been itching to wear this outdoor garb ever since

I'd been given it. Jenny walked over to one of the filing cabinets and pulled out a large pile of folders containing patient records, which she passed on to me. The files were thick and heavy, and I was holding around eight sets of notes which weighed me down slightly.

Jenny picked up her Gladstone bag, which made her look very much like something out of the 1960s, and I followed her out of the building.

'The storeroom downstairs contains lots of equipment for the patients that need it, but I'll show you that later. We really need to get on with our first visit. It's someone I haven't seen before and they live on a farm which I'm told is quite difficult to find.'

Jenny opened the boot of her Ford Fiesta and I gulped as I registered the contents. There was barely any room to add anything to what was already stuffed in there, but Jenny somehow managed to shove her bag towards the back in amongst the melee. It was like a mini hospital room. There were dressing packs, incontinence sheets, boxes of syringes and needles, and a huge yellow sharps box for contaminated waste. I wondered if it would pass any hygiene tests as I could see dog hairs spilling over from the backseat and decided not to dwell on it. I was to learn this was quite normal for district nurses and community nurses in the early 1980s.

'Put the notes in there,' she instructed, 'and you can put your handbag in there too.'

I wasn't at all keen to put my handbag in amongst this lot, but I was left with little choice so I gingerly placed it to the left of a large box containing who knows what? Then I got into the passenger side of the car after moving various items, including crisp packets, chocolate wrappers and other rubbish, off the seat.

'Sorry,' she said. 'We only got back from holiday yesterday and I haven't had time to clean the car. Only just had time to put all the stuff back in this morning before heading here. It's not always like this, trust me.'

I was relieved to hear she didn't take incontinence sheets on holiday and I wanted to trust her, but suspected that it actually was always like this. And of course, I was right; certainly for the four weeks I was working with Jenny, the vehicle was more of a train wreck than a car.

That aside, Jenny was perfect in every other way and, like all nurses of that time, she diligently washed her hands at regular intervals – not always in patient houses, for good reason. One of the major lessons about working in the community was discovering that sometimes you would have to take your shoes off after leaving the house rather than on the way in.

Jenny handed me her diary, started the engine and took off as if she was a rally driver heading for pole position. I fastened my seatbelt quickly, thankful that mandatory seatbelt wearing had just come into force for drivers and front-seat passengers, and gripped the sides of the chair as Jenny lunged through the gears, oblivious. She didn't seem to understand the correct way of slowing down; she would go from fourth gear to slamming on the brakes rather than waste time or energy moving through gears. I was once again grateful that I'd spent three months in Asia before starting the course because, in spite of Jenny's driving being reckless at best, there really was no comparison. In Thailand and India, it seemed compulsory for drivers to harbour a death wish.

Jenny also had a habit of turning her head to look at me when she was speaking for way longer than I felt was safe, irrespective of the fact that she was driving at a rate of knots. I soon discovered that community nursing was a lonely occupation in many ways, so almost all of the staff were pleased to have company in the car and someone to chat to. And chat they did!

I was pleased that Jenny did pull in to consult the map when it became clear she was not sure where she was going. After satisfying herself she knew the route, she drove for another three miles.

'There should be a turnoff to the left after a shop,' she said. 'If you could look out for that and let me know when you see it coming. Apparently it's behind a green and we turn when you see a row of boxes, so it should be easy enough to spot.'

I was just wondering why people would leave a row of boxes out in the middle of nowhere when

Jenny swerved quickly to the left, skidding as she did so. I once again held on for dear life.

'Didn't you see them?' she asked.

'No, I didn't see any boxes,' I answered, puzzled.

Jenny suddenly burst out laughing and looked at me.

'You don't know what boxes are, do you?'

Thinking she'd really lost her marbles and offended by her accusation, I was about to protest that I had not seen any boxes lying in the road when she continued.

'Box hedges, Dawn. You city people are all alike, no idea what goes on in the countryside.' She then regaled me with her opinion of "city people". I had to admit she was right about me as, in spite of my occasional trips into the rural world, most of my life had been spent in Leicester and London, neither of which could be considered nature reserves. I had in fact seen many box hedges in my life; I just didn't realise they were called "boxes" by people in the know.

We continued along a track of about a mile, consisting of bumps and potholes which Jenny didn't seem to notice nor feel the need to slow down for. Her driving continued in the same manner in which it had started, and I would have loved to have given her a lecture on driving safely. She wouldn't have survived a day in the city. At least we city people knew a little about road safety.

It was a bright sunny day in early May. When we pulled up in front of the large farmhouse, we could hear dogs barking in the distance and I could see cows in a field off to the left. Jenny had parked in a large courtyard, if you could call it that, surrounded by barns and sheds.

Jenny got out first and kindly warned me to watch my step. I realised what she meant when I opened the car door. Having just about recovered from the bouncing journey along the drive followed by the emergency stop in the courtyard, I looked around and discovered large dollops of horse manure at various intervals along the way towards the farmhouse. It was like a game of hopscotch, making our way to the door of the farmhouse as we tried to avoid anything that we wouldn't want to stand in.

Jenny knocked on the door. There was no reply, so she just opened it and walked in.

'Hello, district nurse. May we come in?' she called.

We're already in, I thought, but didn't feel I should split hairs.

In the distance we heard a frail woman's voice and we headed towards the sound. The farmhouse was old but well-kept with lots of family photos, old and new, lining the walls. I was a bit disconcerted when I saw a glass cabinet containing around five rifles, but when I nudged Jenny and nodded towards it, she just smirked and rolled her eyes, giving me that "city girls don't understand" look again, and continued through into the lounge.

'Hello, are you Mrs Benson?'

'Yes, Sister. I don't know why they called you, I am managing this leg just fine on my own.'

Jenny gave me a knowing wink and headed towards a large upright chair in which the woman sat. The smell in the room gave away the fact that she was clearly not managing the leg on her own.

Mrs Benson had a ruddy and deeply wrinkled face that told the story of an outdoor life. I looked at the letter Jenny had handed me after getting out of the car and saw she was eighty-six years old. She sat in the sturdy armchair, dressed in a long pink silk nightgown. Over that she had on a bright blue dressing gown. Jenny sat beside her on a wooden dining chair and motioned me to pull up another one from a nearby dining table.

'Well, now I'm here, Mrs Benson, I might as well take look,' said Jenny in a friendly voice that would have put anyone at ease. Anyone who hadn't spent any time in her car, that is.

'I suppose you may as well,' Mrs Benson conceded.

Jenny wrote a few notes down in her diary and pulled out a brand-new folder from the Gladstone bag before suggesting that I remove the bandages. Thankful for something to do, I asked Mrs Benson if I could go and wash my hands in her kitchen and, having been given permission, I returned a few minutes later and began removing the crêpe bandages that had clearly come from a first-aid kit. It was obvious from the discharge and the unmistakeable smell what I was going to find, and that it would not be pretty. Thankful for a previous experience involving maggots, I felt that nothing could be worse than that.

How wrong can you be?

After I'd removed three layers of crêpe bandages soaked in bodily fluids, some of which I suspected might be urine, the odour became so much worse that even Jenny began to look a little concerned. As I delved deeper and deeper through the quagmire of bandages, I eventually revealed a mass of slough with deep ulcers covering the whole of the leg from mid-calf down to the foot. The foot was gangrenous with the toes barely held together by exposed bone.

'Mrs Benson, is your daughter – the one who phoned me – around?' Jenny asked.

'Yeah, you should find her out in the milking shed cleaning up.' She nodded towards the backdoor.

'We're just going to go out and have a little chat with her, we'll be back in a minute.'

We left Mrs Benson's leg resting on a stool on top of a sterile sheet that I'd taken from the dressing pack Jenny had given me.

'She needs to go in,' Jenny said as we headed outside.

Understatement of the year, I thought. "Going in" meant into hospital, and from what I'd seen, Mrs Benson would be very lucky to get away with a below knee amputation.

We eventually found Mrs Benson's daughter and Jenny explained the situation, suggesting that she go and prepare the old lady for a lengthy hospital admission and pack her bags. The daughter, Annette, explained that her mum had flatly refused to have anyone come out to her, especially the GP whom she called Dr Death. This was not for any reason other than she felt that all doctors were too familiar with death and she didn't want to be among those sort of people.

'She's always been independent, not been to a doctor in years.'

Annette told us she ran the farm with the aid of her nephew. She seemed genuinely concerned about her mother, and a little angry.

'I knew it!' she shouted to no-one in particular. 'I told her it would come to this. I told her she would end up in hospital, but she just wouldn't listen.'

Jenny nodded sympathetically and patted Annette on the shoulder before excusing herself to call the doctor and arrange admission. She asked for permission to use the farmhouse telephone to make the call. As Jenny left, Annette stopped suddenly with tears in her eyes and looked at me.

'She isn't going to survive this, is she?' Before I could bring myself to say anything, Annette pulled herself together and marched stoically into the house to tell her rebellious mother that she would have to go into hospital. I could hear the argument developing and left them for a while before making my way back to the room where Mrs Benson was still flatly refusing to be removed from her home of eighty-six years.

'I was born here, I'll die here. You're not moving me.' The old lady's jaw stood out, showing her determination.

Jenny returned and we breathed a sigh of relief. Annette battled back tears and went to pack her mother's bags. It was obvious that Jenny had come across this sort of situation many times before. She sat beside Mrs Benson and calmly explained that there was nothing anyone could do out here and that she would need antibiotics that only hospitals possessed. Carefully avoiding the subject of the life-saving surgery that would be required, she convinced Mrs Benson that the only way to treat this leg would be to go into hospital.

Mrs Benson wasn't daft, though. She asked plainly, 'Will I need an operation?'

Jenny then explained that she might need a small operation, but the doctors would need to decide that. As Jenny told Mrs Benson she would be home in no time, I stared at her disbelievingly, but managed to hide the look so that no-one else noticed. These were the days when health professionals were economical with the truth.

As we left the farmhouse, Jenny gave me a knowing look. 'What do you want me to do, tell her that she is unlikely to come out at all, and that if she does survive surgery, she'll be minus a leg?'

I silently got in the car. Not a great first visit; I felt truly sad that a woman who had managed to avoid doctors for most of her life would most likely end her days on a hospital ward or under the knife, and I still had the stench of gangrene filling my nostrils. At least it would take my mind off Jenny's driving.

I soon discovered that district nurses' rounds incorporated coffee breaks and our next visit was a regular coffee stop, a fix we both needed. As soon as we arrived, Mrs Blake put the kettle on while Jenny got ready to treat her husband's leg ulcers.

Jenny explained that it was always better to catch the ulcers early so that treatment could be started when they would be much more likely to heal. Mr Blake had venous ulcers covering the front of his leg, from the top of the shin down to and around the ankle, and Jenny proudly explained that these were much better now. I nodded and marvelled at her optimism.

After redressing the leg and drinking coffee accompanied by biscuits, we left the Blakes' house feeling much better.

Chapter 7

Dressings Galore

Community nursing consisted of continuous rounds of dressings, mainly due to the scourge at the time of chronic leg ulcers, many of which would never heal. Treatments have moved on now, but back in those days there was little promise of healing once the ulcers had spread up the legs. Many years later, whenever I saw the Queen Mother on television, I noticed only the telltale bandages that covered her lower legs, a dead giveaway that she suffered from leg ulcers.

It was my third day of working with Jenny and I was getting the hang of her driving. Well at least, I was getting the hang of ensuring my seatbelt was always fastened and that there were no objects that could fly at me when she slammed on the brakes. I'd learned a valuable lesson on day one after I'd got fed up with carrying her diary on my lap and placed it on the dashboard – big mistake. She was about to fly around a bend when she'd spotted a pheasant in the road and screeched to a halt. The diary flew off the dash and almost decapitated me. Okay, I exaggerate slightly, but I did check my neck a few times that day to see if all was where it should be. The pheasant had given Jenny a long stare before continuing on its way, but it was nothing compared to my glare.

She'd laughed, clearly not noticing my pallor. 'I should have run it over. You can eat them if you kill them by accident, you know.'

Back to my third day. We were on our way to see a young paraplegic man with pressure sores to his buttocks. Daniel Gray, aged twenty-three, had been involved in a motorcycle accident and broken his back when he came off and was thrown against a wall. After spending some months in Stoke Mandeville Hospital, which specialised in spinal injuries, he had been discharged. He now lived in a small bungalow a few miles away from his family home.

Since his discharge, Jenny told me, he had gained weight and neglected to change position often enough to prevent pressure sores developing. His attitude was if you couldn't feel it, it wasn't worth worrying about. Life had dealt him a hard blow and he was very bitter about it.

Jenny explained that his family had told her he had always been a self-absorbed character and the accident had only added to his general belief that somehow the world owed him. The family relationships had completely broken down following his accident as he no longer tried to curb his behaviour and deliberately sought to insult or offend everyone he met, including the district nurses. He was wasting his time with Jenny; it was like water off a duck's back.

'Who's this now?' he asked, obviously meaning me.

'This is Dawn, a student nurse who's out with me. I can ask her to wait in the car if you'd prefer.'

'No, she might as well stay. I mean, I'm like a monkey in a cage, after all.' He performed a 180° turn in his wheelchair and headed towards a room at the back of the bungalow. We followed, but not before I'd taken in the mess surrounding me. It made Jenny's car look positively pristine.

Clothes littered the floor; Daniel obviously didn't feel the need to put them away after he took them off. Cigarette butts filled an ashtray on a table and stale cigarette smoke hung in the air. There was a settee, barely visible underneath crisp and chocolate packets. Dirty washing from the kitchen overflowed into the lounge.

We arrived in what turned out to be Daniel's bedroom where he heaved himself from the wheelchair on to the bed.

Jenny turned to me. 'You're in there.' She nodded towards the kitchen.

'You're kidding?' I mouthed, scowling. I was here to dress his backside, not to be kitchen maid.

'He won't let you do his dressing anyway, and no-one else will do it,' she said quietly, pleading with her eyes.

I sighed and stomped into the kitchen and began removing the crockery from the overflowing sink. Before I could even begin to do any washing up, I heard shouting and swearing coming from the bedroom, which made me smile. Perhaps I'd got the better share of this particular deal.

After filling a bin with chip wrappers, crisp packets and all manner of other nasties, as well as driving a few flies away from their feasts, I started on the washing up. Jenny was in the lounge by this time, picking up clothes, and she brought them through to put into the washing machine.

'Where is he?' I asked.

'On the bed on his side. It's the only time I can get him to relieve the pressure on his sores. He won't do bed rest, so we reached a compromise after everyone else who ever came here pulled out because of his rudeness: he stays on the bed while I clear up. It's not ideal, but even social and voluntary services have given up on him, and they rightly argue that he is quite capable of clearing up after himself. He just won't.'

'Can they do that? Social Services, I mean.'

'They say he's a danger to himself and to their staff. He's well able to look after himself if he so chooses, and his refusal doesn't constitute "need". He's his own worst enemy.'

'I can f***ing hear you in there.'

'Well, ain't that a shame!' laughed Jenny.

'Condescending cow!' came the retort.

This friendly (on Jenny's part) banter continued for an hour, until Jenny shouted, 'Cheerio, Danny. See you Thursday.'

'It's not f***ing Danny, it's Dan, you twat.'

Jenny put two fingers up on the way out, but obviously not in sight of Dan.

'Why didn't you warn me?' I asked when we got back in the car.

'Warn you about what?' She laughed at her own joke.

Following my introduction to Dan, who I'm pleased to say I never met again, Jenny took me to his polar opposite. A pleasant thirty-year-old woman had also sustained spinal injuries, but hers came after falling from a horse. The house she lived in was in the next village and couldn't have been cleaner. She lived alone as her husband couldn't cope with her disability and had left the family home a few years earlier, although he still paid the mortgage.

'Guilt,' suggested Jenny when I asked why.

There wasn't a bitter bone in Debbie Price's body. She radiated joy, demonstrating that we are all different. There's no point trying to understand why some people are pleasant and others are just plain obnoxious when they are handed the same cards in life.

We were there to change Debbie's catheter, and this time I was allowed to carry out the procedure. A long-term indwelling catheter had become part of Debbie's life and it was changed every eight weeks. Usually catheters were changed twelve weekly, but serious complications can occur from blocked catheters when someone has the type of paraplegia that Debbie had.

'If we leave it too late and the catheter blocks, she can get autonomic dysreflexia,' Jenny explained.

'What's that?'

Debbie took over the explanation. 'My blood pressure could go through the roof and I could end up fitting or even dying,' she said nonchalantly.

'Wow! Has that ever happened?'

'Only once for me, but it's pretty terrifying. I have to call 999 and take these tablets.' She showed me a packet of Nifedipine, an anti-hypertensive drug I was familiar with from my cardio-thoracic days. 'The quickest way to treat it is to deal with the cause, which in my case is either a blocked catheter or constipation. I manage the bowels myself with tablets.'

I smiled. 'That would do the trick.'

I had changed plenty of catheters during my nurse training course to date and as an enrolled nurse at the London Chest Hospital, but I'd never done this in a patient's own home. I looked around fearfully. Where was my dressing trolley?

As if reading my mind, Jenny cleared the top of Debbie's bedside table and gave it a wipe with a duster before opening a dressing pack. I gawped, as we hadn't swabbed the surface with a sterile cleansing wipe.

'We have to adapt when in people's homes,' she explained. 'Remember it's their own bacteria, not from a bunch of strangers. We make it as sterile as possible, though.'

I washed my hands and returned to open up the pack before donning sterile gloves, while Jenny removed the water from the balloon holding the old catheter in place, using a syringe to do so. She then pulled gently at the catheter; because Debbie couldn't feel pain, Jenny could cause internal damage if she was too rough. No need for worry, though, as the catheter slipped out with ease.

In the early 1980s women were not given local anaesthetic for catheterisation, the reasoning being that because the urethra is shorter than in men and there is no prostate gland involved, they wouldn't feel pain. It's true that some didn't, but some did. In this case, Debbie would not feel pain, but thankfully women are offered local anaesthetic in the modern era.

On a similar topic, female nurses did catheterise men in some hospitals, but there was no nationally adopted practice. In some hospitals it wasn't allowed. In the hospitals I worked in, it was to be introduced at a later date as the shortage of male nurses meant calling a doctor on to the wards to re-catheterise men at all hours of the day and night. Often the doctor called would be female, which highlighted the ridiculousness of the situation.

Catheterising women is, in fact, more difficult as the urethra can be hidden, particularly when women are on the larger side. I've spent many occasions delving (not literally) into the depths of darkness of a woman's anatomy with a torch in search of the pesky little hole that is the urethra. It is not unusual for junior nurses and medical students to try to catheterise a clitoris or shove the catheter into the vagina, thinking they are in the right place.

With only one hole, it is far easier to find the right place to catheterise a man. Erections, however, are another matter. It behoves a nurse to get on with the job as quickly as possible to spare any embarrassment on either side in such cases.

There were no such problems with Debbie's catheter. Once I had become used to the unfamiliar surroundings and adjusted to accepting the limitations concerning the lack of hospital equipment, it was a simple procedure. Many women with spinal injuries nowadays have suprapubic catheters inserted into a hole created by a surgical incision just above the pubic bone. Such catheters are less likely to cause infection and are often easier to manage for patients, particularly those who are sexually active. Sex is possible for people with indwelling catheters, but it requires a little more planning and effort. Sex for people with spinal injuries lacks the sensation of orgasm, but many men and women continue with sexual relations for the partner's sake and for the intimacy.

After leaving Debbie's home, I was feeling much happier.

'Talk about opposites,' I remarked.

'Welcome to the community, Dawn. The thing about hospitals is that you can get rid of your patients by sending them home. Out here, we are stuck with them, so we try to build up a relationship with the likes of Dan. He's unlikely to change until they bring in personality transplants, but there's not much point aggravating him, except when I get fed up with him. But I don't ever cross the line.'

Wise words from an experienced district nurse.

Chapter 8

The Fallout

One of my most bizarre experiences during the community placement came in the third week.

I had worked with most of the nurses in the team by then, including the auxiliaries, and experienced all manner of driving styles and vehicles. It's funny how we always remember odd things – I could tell you every make and model of car I sat in, along with their colours (not that there was much variety back then), but that would be plain boring. Describing the car boots and their contents would be a little more interesting, although the common theme was that no matter how tidy they happened to be, they were all jam packed with every piece of equipment that might conceivably be needed during a visit. This is understandable when you remember the nurses were making forty-minute round trips to visit people in outlying villages and farms.

The car interiors were also interesting. Some had baby seats or crumbs and sweet packets littering the back, indicating the nurse had children or grandchildren. Others had dog hairs plus/minus a dog grill plus/minus said car seats, wrappers and so on. Some were pristine, indicating the nurse was possibly single or minimalistic.

The worst cars were those in which the nurse smoked, ashtrays overflowing with cigarette butts and the cursory 'You don't mind if I smoke, do you?' while lighting up fiasco. I had stopped smoking again myself the year before so I did still understand the addiction and the need to light up at every opportunity. Nevertheless, it was challenging, sometimes because I hated the smell, and at other times because I could have ripped the cigarette right out of their hand, depending on which way the wind was blowing in my world.

Cars and driving styles aside, the majority of the staff were a pleasure to work with and had built good rapports with the patients. Some of them nipped home for lunch – unheard of in hospitals – and others popped into the shop or post office to deal with household chores. I could see the attraction for married women with young children, but they did work hard. Even though it was only Jenny who carried a bleep, which went off constantly, district nurses worked weekends and late shifts as it was a seven-day service.

The patients were pleasant, on the whole, apart from the likes of Dan whom I never would have grown to like. Seeing patients dressed in their own clothes did make a difference to how they were treated, and how they behaved. In the community, to a large extent the patient was in control – it was their home and we were visitors with no right of access, except by invitation.

The homes we visited varied from the tidy to the downright infested. Dogs were as much a hazard to us as they were to postmen. Some dogs were friendly, while others were terrifying. I was always wary of the bigger dogs in spite of being a dog lover, although I was never attacked.

Some patients were chain smokers and we would walk in to a clouded room rather than a crowded one! There will be a lot more detail with regards to working in the community when I write about my days as a qualified district nurse, but suffice it to say for now that it was a very different experience to working within the safe confines of a hospital.

The district nurses planned their day around the patients they visited. For instance, people with possible infectious diseases were visited last thing, as were people living in the dirtiest houses or the heavy smokers. The reasoning was that the nurse could go straight home after that visit, get out of the uniform and take a bath – if they weren't going to Tesco first, that is!

But let's get back to the bizarre experience I alluded to earlier. Jenny thought it would be a good idea for me to work in a GP practice for the day and had arranged for me to spend the morning with a practice nurse. When we arrived at the surgery, there were two separate signs outside: DR M SMITH; DR F JONES, which I thought was slightly unusual, but thought no more of it.

We walked through the door to find two separate windows behind which receptionists sat within the same room, but manning their individual doctor's window. We took the window to the left, where Jenny said hello before leading me through the invisibly divided waiting room along a corridor to the left. By now, Jenny was watching my face and giggling.

'Okay, what's going on?' I asked when we entered an office, also separated into two halves.

'I'll tell you later,' she whispered.

She didn't need to; I'd already guessed, and the practice nurse confirmed my suspicions.

'They fell out five years ago. Since then, they won't speak to each other, and now the receptionists, secretaries, even the patients don't speak to each other when they're in this building.'

'So have the rest of the staff taken sides?'

'No. Outside, everyone behaves normally, but fear of losing their jobs makes them behave as if they have when they're in work. It's stupid – these two doctors are worse than children. I think the patients join in just for fun.'

'What did they fall out about?'

'I'm not sure, I expect it was something trivial. Dr Jones always did fly off the handle; I'm glad I don't work for him, he's always shouting at someone. You'll probably hear him bellowing sometime this morning. I think Dr Smith probably got fed up with his behaviour.'

For someone who wasn't taking sides, she was making it clear whose side she wasn't taking! But then, who's going to bite the hand that feeds them?

Later on, when Jenny came to collect me from this rather peculiar environment, I scolded her. 'You could have warned me!'

'And miss seeing that look on your face? Not likely.' I had grown fond of Jenny, but she had a wicked sense of humour.

'I'm sure I've heard you call both of those doctors about patients.'

'Oh yes, the team works with both, but we have to be discreet because if one catches on that we're seeing more of the other's patients than theirs, they'll invent reasons for us to take on more of theirs. I work round it by sending a different staff nurse to each surgery to discuss patients so they never know what's happening on the other side.'

'Do you know why they fell out?'

'Money, Dawn, it's always money.'

'Or sex,' I said quietly.

'You're too young to know about sex.' She nudged me and cackled loudly.

I was going to miss working with Jenny and her team, but not the twenty-mile drive to work every morning, and certainly not Jenny's driving. I missed the hubbub of hospital life so it would be many years before I seriously considered working in the community again. Once I did venture out, though, I spent the final fifteen years of my nursing career *on the district* in one way or another.

Chapter 9

Mat Unit

The maternity unit was a large separate building with its own car park and ambulance bay, its entrance on the west side of the hospital. It was like a hospital within a hospital, with its own administrative offices, library, school of midwifery and outpatients departments on the ground floor. The labour ward and theatres were on the first floor, and antenatal and postnatal wards on the second.

I made a mistake in terminology on my first day and suffered a quick reprimand I wouldn't forget.

'We are not nurses, we are midwives,' said the rather rotund sister. The truth was that once nurses became midwives, they argued that midwives were very different to nurses, and who was I to disagree? In the early 1980s, a nurse who wanted to become a midwife did an extra year's training (later that decade it was extended to eighteen months, shortly before I began training to be a midwife in the mid-1980s). On completion of the training they became registered midwives (RMs), but also kept their nurse registration. Nowadays, many midwives enter through a direct-entry training programme.

As a student nurse, I found the labour ward placement particularly dull. Not because seeing babies being delivered wasn't fascinating – it was, and I did manage to see the required five births that were a mandatory part of my training in order to pass the placement, but we were always at the back of the queue when it came to seeing anything. Ahead of us were student midwives, medical students, junior doctors, and basically the world and its brother. On top of that, we were not allowed to *do* anything except check blood pressures, test urine and palpate the mandatory five pregnant abdomens, which made for long and boring shifts. I couldn't even speak to women in labour, perhaps because they had other things on their minds, but it didn't help the days go any more quickly on the ward. Years later, when I was a midwife, the labour ward was my favourite place of work and I was promoted to midwifery sister, working on one of the busiest labour wards in the country.

Each labour room had a door – obviously – and a small square window decorated with frosted glass stripes, allowing just enough clear glass for the midwife in charge to take a peek through without intruding on what was going on inside the room. One afternoon I was accompanying the midwifery sister along the corridor and we peeked into one of the rooms from which we could hear a lot of noise, although it wasn't unusual to hear the "cry of the banshee" coming from labour rooms. A father-to-be stood at the foot of the bed and the midwife was gowned up and proficiently delivering the baby while looked on. Then I blinked, and he'd disappeared. One minute he was there, the next, he was gone.

The sister I was with chuckled. 'Whoops, there goes another one.'

Upon opening the door, we saw the woman who had just given birth cuddling her newborn. She rolled her eyes at her partner, who was still lying on the floor where he had fainted.

'I knew he shouldn't have come in. My mum would have been much more help.'

We handed the rather pale man a glass of water and helped him up.

'It's a girl,' Sister told him and I caught him before he passed out again. Eventually he sat up and rose from the floor, tears streaming down his face. He leaned over to kiss his wife and inspect his daughter.

'Don't tell your mother,' he said sheepishly.

'I wouldn't dare!' She smiled up at him. 'You tried, that's the main thing.'

After we'd left the doting couple, Sister told me that partners or other accompanying individuals were told that if they were going to pass out, they should leave the room as the midwife would not have time to deal with them.

'Mother and baby come first,' she said.

For the rest of the day I had visions of the disappearing man and giggled every time I remembered it. By the time I was on my break, I had embellished the story and was recounting it to my colleagues, alongside a practical demonstration to make it a real laughing point.

For student nurses, it was better and more interesting to work on the wards in the maternity unit. As well as being allowed to check the blood pressure of an antenatal mother-to-be, test urine and palpate abdomens, here I was also allowed to speak to people and listen to foetal heartbeats with a Pinard's stethoscope. Obviously, a midwife would check the latter before or after me.

Women were sometimes admitted for bed rest following a diagnosis of pre-eclampsia. Eclampsia is a dangerous condition where a woman can have a seizure due to high blood pressure, which in turn can damage the developing foetus. It was responsible for maternal and foetal deaths before the condition was better understood – who can forget the scene in the popular *Downton Abbey* series that demonstrated the horror of this condition far better than any textbook ever could? The pre-eclampsia condition was, and still is, taken very seriously, but thankfully I never witnessed an eclamptic fit during my student nurse days.

My favourite part of the maternity placement in the hospital was working on the postnatal ward as I got to be a lot more hands-on with both mothers and babies. I was taught to help mums with breastfeeding – not that I had a clue what to do, but I was slightly ahead of most first-time mums. The best people to learn from were the experienced mums who had just given birth to second or third babies, and in some cases sixth or seventh.

Many women in the early 1980s gave up quickly on breastfeeding as bottle feeding was deemed easier and was fashionable. The "breast is best" philosophy was in its infancy with an almost evangelical drive occurring a decade or so later. I secretly and rather selfishly loved it when a mother chose to bottle feed because I got to feed the tiny little babies, stashed away in the nursery while Mum had a kip. Some mothers opted to keep their babies by the bedside so they could feed them for themselves, but others were glad of the rest, particularly after a difficult labour. And hard labour delivering a baby was for many.

Four hourly feeding was the recommendation of the day. Feeding regimes, like many other health regimes, are an ever moving feast as new guidelines or the latest research is published. If a mother chose to feed her baby for herself, she would be woken up in the early hours of the morning to give the infant its four hourly feed, come what may. The majority of women who weren't breastfeeding opted to have their babies go to the nursery during the night so they could get some sleep, but the stalwarts persevered, much to the chagrin of the other women who would complain at being woken up by someone else's baby while the actual mother slept through the racket.

Babies got used to the four hourly feeding regime and would strike up with a cacophony of shrieks at the allotted time. Like an orchestra tuning up, they would cry out a universal chorus of discordant and chaotic wailing – not that orchestras tuning up are chaotic.

Visiting time was restricted to a couple of hours each morning and the same in the evening, and limited to two visitors at a time. In spite of this, the rules were occasionally relaxed to allow a third person in, but had to be curtailed when the noise of cooing parents, grandparents and small children in the postnatal ward became too much.

It was quite obvious who the new fathers were, not only because they beamed with pride at managing to father a small miracle, but because they had no idea how to handle said miracle. Some nervously took hold of the fragile being as if it was an egg that would crack at any moment; others picked it up and handled it as if it ought to be able to play football by now, and a midwife would quickly intervene and explain how delicate the baby was and how to handle it correctly. Yet others would hold the child at arms' length. One could never tell whether this was because they were worried about handling it or frightened of the curdled milk that was always lurking, waiting for the next shoulder to deposit itself on, which certainly wouldn't have helped the new fathers who looked like they had been out on the town, "wetting the baby's head" all night.

Inexperienced mums weren't always adept with nappy changes, either, and urine and other excreta was often deposited on an unsuspecting relative's hand or clothing. Disposable nappies weren't as commonplace as they are today, and so all new mums were taught to change and fold towelling nappies.

Personally, I enjoyed nappy changing; it gave me something to do, and once I'd mastered the art, I was allowed to demonstrate it to anyone willing to listen. New mums were like sponges, gazing at me and listening to my every word. The only problem was that sometimes pregnancy appeared to affect the memory and my every word went in one ear and out the other – a bit like the milk that went in one end of the baby and out the other at alarming speed!

Anyone who has worked with new mothers, or indeed been a parent, will know what I mean when I mention the "third-day blues", or "baby blues" as it was sometimes referred to. I had been working on the postnatal ward for – you guessed it – three days when I had my first experience of blubbering mums. It was as if someone had turned on an invisible tap and the women were unable to find the off switch. I might be exaggerating as not every new mum experiences the third-day blues, and its effects are as wide and varied as the mums themselves. Some women experience something far worse than this, leading to postnatal depression or puerperal psychosis. I'll discuss an experience I had of a poor woman with the latter in the next chapter, but for now, I'm simply talking about baby blues, which is a very mild form of depression resulting in mood swings following postnatal hormone changes.

Before undertaking my maternity placement, I had been given lectures on pregnancy and childbirth, but mental health was skimmed over. Baby blues had been mentioned, but not in any detail. All I knew was that women could feel low for a brief period around the third or fourth day postpartum. What I didn't realise was how useless and guilty this could make a new mother feel or how easily a bout of tears could be triggered. Many women tried to hide their feelings, but they couldn't.

The guilt came from women believing they should be happy all the time because they had had a baby. These feelings, coupled with lack of sleep, pain from perineal suturing and/or caesarean scars, bruising and/or sore nipples, could lead to feelings of helplessness and inadequacy. Sometimes, it was the family that bore the brunt of these mood swings, and at other times a new mother might ignore the baby, almost blaming the newborn for how they were feeling. For most women, these feelings only lasted around a day or two, and nurses and midwives would provide reassurance during this time. In rare cases, though, a woman would become excessively paranoid and agitated.

Josie was one such woman.

Chapter 10

Tired Eyes Do Matter, Don't They?

Josie was a twenty-eight-year-old first-time mother. Her baby, Christine, had been born normally following a lengthy thirty-hour labour. An episiotomy (cutting of the perineum with scissors) had been performed during the birth to prevent a large tear. Christine weighed in at eight pounds, three ounces and had a beautiful crop of black hair. Both Josie and Simon, her husband, were delighted by the birth of their daughter, and although Christine was a demanding and voracious feeder, everything appeared perfect until day three.

Josie was looking haggard and bedraggled. The other mums said she had been disturbing them in the night, then she started to imagine that all the other women were talking about her behind her back. By day four, she was becoming more and more agitated and paranoid, and her handling of Christine was a little rough.

Initially, the midwives had put her behaviour down to third-day blues, but now it was becoming bizarre. I was helping a mum breastfeed from the bed opposite when I saw Josie pick up Christine. Her eyes told me she was psychotic and, just before she could drop the baby on the floor, I dashed over and caught her.

Doctors were called, and then a specialist psychiatrist. Josie was displaying signs of a thankfully very rare condition called puerperal psychosis, where a woman becomes severely mentally ill following childbirth. The decision was taken to move both her and Christine to a mother-and-baby unit at the nearest psychiatric hospital for assessment and specialist supervision.

The psychiatrist called Josie's husband and explained the situation. I was chosen to escort her to the psychiatric hospital in the ambulance, along with Christine.

Josie was clearly bemused at what was happening, but not in this world. Almost as soon as we got into the ambulance, she turned to me and spoke.

'Tired eyes do matter, don't they?'

The thing was, she didn't say it once; she repeated it over and over again for the whole of the forty-five minute drive. By the time we arrived at the hospital, my brain was addled and I was beginning to feel like I was being hypnotised.

I was looking forward to being able to discharge my responsibility – I was way out of my depth – and get a lift back with the ambulance crew. Unfortunately for me, escort transfers could be a pain for nurses because sometimes we were taken miles away, and then the ambulance would be called off to another emergency and the crew couldn't wait.

This was one of those occasions.

'Sorry, love. We'll let dispatch know where you are.' I groaned inside, knowing this could mean hours before another ambulance happened to be in the vicinity, as they wouldn't send one especially to pick up a nurse.

I was led towards the mother-and-baby unit and things went from bad to worse. There was no psychiatric nurse available to admit Josie and I couldn't leave her alone with Christine as it wouldn't have been safe. After another ninety minutes of the 'Tired eyes do matter, don't they?' mantra, I was beside myself. As much as I felt sorry for Josie, I knew those words would be embedded in my brain forever, and I was right. As I write this, I am back in that small holding room, Christine in my arms, having to answer, 'Yes, they do,' every time I heard the question and Josie looked at me. I tried not answering, but then her eyes became wild and she looked like she might jump on me – or worse, Christine – at any moment.

'Tired eyes do matter, don't they?'

'Yes, Josie, they do.'

'Tired eyes do matter, don't they?'

'Yes, Josie, they do.'

'Tired eyes do matter, don't they?'

'Yes, Josie, they do.'

And so on, and so on.

Finally, when I felt I could stand it no more, a psychiatrist came in, accompanied by a psychiatric nurse.

'An ambulance is here to take you home,' the nurse said to me.

I leapt off the chair, thrust the baby into the astonished nurse's arms and ran for my life.

The tragedy of a woman suffering from puerperal psychosis is that prior to giving birth, they often show no signs of mental illness. The condition ranges from mild to severe, but women displaying symptoms invariably need specialist treatment. Most women recover after appropriate period of treatment. I'm not certain whether Josie was one of these, but there is no reason to assume she wasn't. The main problem is that around half of women developing the condition will suffer the same illness following subsequent births, but at least they are monitored closely throughout pregnancy and postnatal.

And just for the record, tired eyes do matter!

Chapter 11

Community Midwife

Rosemary was a community midwife, and also a member of the church I had started to go to, although I hadn't got to know her through church. Because I worked the majority of weekends and late shifts, it prevented me from going out to too many social gatherings in the evenings.

Rosemary was one of the most bubbly people I have had the good fortune to work with, and a force to be reckoned with. From the moment she picked me up from the hospital reception, I knew we would get on. Her larger-than-life personality showed itself in every way, and because she was always happy, her demeanour would calm anyone's nerves. The women on her books were immediately put at ease on first meeting her.

Her driving was something else, though, similar to Jenny's. The district nurse and Rosemary could have been related, and I wondered if community nurses/midwives were actually frustrated ambulance drivers.

The difference between Rosemary and Jenny was that their car boots were complete opposites. Rosemary had a Gladstone bag, but the only other item she carried in her boot was a set of baby weighing scales. Her car, though not immaculate, was immeasurably cleaner than Jenny's and contained no dog hairs!

After being in the car with Rosemary for around ten minutes, I heard her laugh for the first time. Like her personality, that laugh was unforgettable.

The morning consisted of visiting postnatal mothers and babies. 'We visit daily for ten days, but can visit for up to twenty-eight days. If all is well we discharge to the health visitor between ten and fourteen days,' she explained. I was interested to see how new and experienced mums coped once they were at home as most of them were discharged from hospital between two and seven days post-delivery.

Rosemary's patch encompassed a suburban area of the town comprising mostly financially stable households. The first house we arrived at was on a relatively new estate where all the houses looked the same.

'Cardboard boxes,' commented Rosemary with that wonderful laugh I was already growing to love.

A bedraggled-looking man answered the door and almost hugged her. 'I'm so pleased you're here, we can't stop her crying.' As he led us through to the lounge – not that we needed leading, we just had to follow the wails from the unhappy infant – Rosemary mouthed to me that they were first-time parents.

A tired-looking woman of twenty-nine was pacing the room, frantically trying to calm the baby.

'There, there, everything's alright,' she said in a rather manic tone that didn't have an ounce of conviction. As soon as she saw Rosemary, she gave a huge sigh of relief. 'She's been like this all night. I've fed her until my nipples are sore.'

Looking at this frantic woman, I believed her. She still had her nightdress on, one breast hanging out of a nursing bra that remained unfastened. It really did look sore – raw, in fact.

'This is Dawn, she's a student nurse. Do you mind her being here?' This was a question Rosemary always asked, I discovered. In this instance, I would have been tempted to grab the screaming child from the mother's arms, but Rosemary's calm voice had the desired effect on both mother and baby.

'No, that's fine.'

'This is Mary, Donald, and this little mite is Joanna.'

What this conversation did, Rosemary explained to me later, was to distract Mary and calm her nerves. Once Mary was calm, Joanna, in turn, stopped crying.

'Babies sense stress in parents and they need to feel secure.' This statement turned out to be true in the majority of cases, as long as the baby was feeding enough, didn't have wind and wasn't wearing a dirty nappy.

Rosemary and I washed our hands, and then she took the baby and examined the umbilical cord, which had its clamp still in place as she was only five days old. Most cords dropped off after seven to fourteen days once they had dried out and shrivelled, but it was important to check that no infection was developing in the area. Rosemary also checked the baby's skin and felt gently over the two fontanelles or soft spots on her head. The fontanelles would gradually fuse together over time, but they were necessary, Rosemary explained to me, as they enabled the bones to move as the baby went through the birth canal and would allow the brain to grow.

After finishing with Joanna and holding her for a few minutes until she fell asleep, Rosemary laid her down in her crib.

'You're going to need to cream that nipple for a few days. Do you have any nipple protectors?'

'Yes, Donald bought some yesterday.'

'I don't think she's latching on properly. That's why you're sore, and probably why she's fractious. Dawn and I will go and see a few more people, and then come back and help you feed her.'

The relief on Mary and Donald's faces was priceless to see.

'Thank you, Rosemary.'

'No problem. You go and get washed and dressed while she's asleep. Donald will keep an eye on her, won't you?'

The anxious-looking man who had answered the door now appeared much calmer himself and he nodded confidently. 'Of course I will. You go, love.'

Once outside, Rosemary explained that she needed to talk through some other things with the new parents and check Mary's perineum was healing as she'd had stitches. She would also ask about vaginal discharge and examine the uterus, referred to as the fundus, that would take six to ten weeks to return to normal size. I realised then that there was a lot more to midwifery than delivering babies.

'Midwife, Dawn. The term comes from the old English and means "with woman".' I could see how appropriate that term was, although it seemed from meeting Donald that new fathers needed just as much assistance post-delivery.

The morning passed by quickly. We visited another three babies and their mums, two of whom had other children and required little in the way of assistance. I observed as Rosemary discussed feeding, weight, maternal physical and mental health. Where a partner or parent was present, Rosemary included them, but also ensured she got time alone with each mother while they, or I, were left holding the baby – literally.

Rosemary explained before we visited the final couple with their first child that she suspected domestic violence, but the woman was unwilling to acknowledge this to her, in spite of multiple "accidents" during pregnancy resulting in bruises that could not easily be explained away.

'My concern now is for both the mother and the baby,' said Rosemary. 'After I've checked the baby over, I'm going to take Marion upstairs on the pretext of teaching you, so he'll have to stay downstairs and watch over Jake, the newborn.'

With this plan in mind, I was to ask lots of questions in order to distract the partner, who had managed to avoid meeting Rosemary antenatally, and come across as an overly keen student.

Rosemary rang the doorbell, but there was no reply. We waited, still nothing.

'Marion told me he drives a BMW so that's his car. We know he's in.'

As I looked at the BMW in the driveway and the large detached house, my expression must have been a dead giveaway.

'Domestic violence is not confined to the working classes,' she whispered while ringing the doorbell again, this time more persistently, keeping her finger on the bell.

I stepped back on to the driveway and saw a curtain upstairs move briefly. The man saw that he had been rumbled and answered the door shortly afterwards.

'I do apologise, I forgot you were coming this morning. Marion's not feeling so good, she had a fall in the night. Must have been tired, she's just gone back to sleep. Can you come back later?'

'I'm so sorry, Mr Fletcher, but we have to help someone with feeding after this visit, and then I'm in clinic all afternoon. Actually, if you don't mind, I'm desperate for the loo. Could I use yours?'

He looked uncomfortable.

'Nice to meet you, by the way,' Rosemary continued. 'We spoke on the phone. This is Dawn, a student nurse. Perhaps she could take a look at little Jake while I nip to the loo.'

'Of course. Come in. The toilet's through there.' He nodded to a downstairs toilet.

'Now you mention it, I'm desperate too,' I lied.

'You go down, I'll go up, if that's alright?' Rosemary's face was the picture of innocence.

Mr Fletcher coughed. 'Upstairs on the left.'

At that moment, the telephone in the hallway rang and he went to answer it. Rosemary shot upstairs like a panther and I went for my imaginary wee in the downstairs loo, being as quick as would seem appropriate so that I could distract Mr Fletcher when I came out. My distraction was not required, though; he was still speaking in angry muffled tones on the phone when Rosemary called from upstairs.

'Marion's awake now, Dawn. Come on up, I know you want to see little Jake.'

Mr Fletcher was too engrossed in his heated telephone conversation to pay us any attention. I walked into the bedroom and Rosemary motioned for me to close the door. The woman attending to her crying baby was sporting a huge black eye and multiple bruises to her upper arms.

Rosemary put her arm around her. 'You don't have to put up with this, you know. We can get help.'

The fear-filled eyes spoke volumes. It was not the first time I had come across domestic violence and sadly it wouldn't be the last. Women (and sometimes men) were beaten into submission, usually through verbal and/or physical abuse, until they felt useless.

'He doesn't mean it. Jake was crying and he hasn't had much sleep. He's under a lot of pressure at work.'

Rosemary sighed gently and said, 'And what if this anger spills over on to Jake?'

'He would never hurt Jake, he adores him.'

Footsteps coming upstairs warned us our time was up.

'Please don't say anything.'

The door opened and an angry Mr Fletcher filled the doorway. 'What's going on? I told you she needed some sleep.'

'Sorry,' said Rosemary. 'Little Jake was restless so we popped in and woke Marion by mistake. She's just been telling me about her fall in the night.'

Looking relieved, Mr Fletcher moved over to the bed and put his arm around his wife. 'She's got a bit clumsy since Jake was born, haven't you, love?'

Marion nodded quietly. After examining Jake, Rosemary spoke to the couple.

'Jake's looking well. I'll be handing over to Rebecca, the health visitor, in a few weeks' time. She'll keep an eye on Jake over the next few years.'

Rosemary looked sternly towards Mr Fletcher before turning and leaving the room.

'What happens now?' I asked as we got in the car.

Rosemary sighed deeply, exhaling a long breath. 'I'll report my concerns again to the GP and give a full handover to the health visitor, but without Marion's permission, I can't involve the police. And even if I do, they're not really interested in "domestics", as they call them. Obviously if child abuse is suspected, that's a different matter and we would refer it to social services. Not all abusive partners turn on children, but many do, so I suspect that will happen with Jake in the not too distant future.'

It was not easy working in the community and suspecting domestic violence, and even when we did complain to the police, the culture of the day meant that it wasn't taken seriously enough. Things are mostly different now.

After this visit, Rosemary had to switch back into midwife mode as we drove back to help Mary feed her baby.

'You're just in time,' said a delighted Donald, who answered the door immediately. 'She's just woken. Can I get you both a coffee?'

After what we had just been through, a whisky would have been more appropriate.

'We'd love one, no sugar for me.'

'Nor me,' I answered.

'Now where's that beautiful little girl?'

As I watched Rosemary happily demonstrating how to latch Joanna on to the breast and teaching Mary the art of breastfeeding, I drank my coffee.

'The nipples get sore when the baby isn't latching on properly. They're hungry little mites so they grab the first thing, often the nipple,' explained Rosemary. 'Unfortunately, they don't get enough food this way, so they get tetchy and you get sore.'

Rosemary applied the protector over the nipple, then showed Mary how to get Joanna to suck on the breast. As I watched and learned, I reflected – not for the first time – on how nursing and, it seemed, midwifery were art forms. We did everything we could to make the person in front of us feel like they were the only person in the world and that we had nothing more important to do that day than help them.

This ability to compartmentalise was learned by some nurses early on in their training. For some, it came naturally, and a few never learned it at all, but we were taught right from the start that even if we had stuff going on in our own lives to leave our problems at the door. The best in our profession have mastered this ability to switch off to what has gone before and deal with the here and now. That doesn't mean we don't go home and cry at night – I've been through enough examples of that – but it does mean that we are the best we can be when dealing with people who are at their most vulnerable.

Chapter 12

Twinset and Pearls

Health visitors reading this book might want to skip this chapter as they must be sick and tired of the joke. For those who don't know, though, nurses and midwives back in the day always referred to health visitors as the twinset and pearls brigade – because the majority of them wore a twinset and pearls and no-one knew why. This is no longer the case in my experience –maybe the teasing got too much for them in the end.

Trainee nurses didn't get to spend much time with health visitors, a day or two if we were lucky, but we loved it because we got the opportunity to work out of uniform. When my turn came, I met the health visitor at the front of the hospital as arranged and had to stifle a giggle as a woman in her forties with a mop of curly brown hair arrived to collect me. She didn't need to introduce herself because I recognised her immediately as she was wearing – you guessed it – a twinset and pearls.

After a cursory glance at my attire – plain beige pencil skirt and sky-blue blouse – she introduced herself as Barbara. Her grin told me I would have a good few days working with her.

'Health visiting is all about the promotion of health rather than caring for the sick,' she informed me. I soon learned that health visitors, like midwives, did not like to be called nurses, although they too were qualified nurses who had chosen to undertake a health visiting course, giving them the right to the title. To be honest, in their case, I agreed. The job was nothing like nursing.

For the most part, we visited mums with babies after the midwife had discharged them to the health visitor at 10 days, but parents with children under five also came under the jurisdiction of the health visitor. They worked closely with social services in cases when children were deemed to be at risk, and these cases were by far the most challenging part of their role.

On the first morning we visited around four mother and baby households. The health visitor asked if the mother had any concerns about the child and carried out developmental checks that included playing with toys where there were toddlers, something I was keen to participate in. There was more to it, obviously, as children had developmental milestones to achieve in order to be considered "normal". Those who didn't meet these milestones might be considered to have slow development and come under "learning disability" – now "special needs". Each parent had a Child Health Record book and most diligently produced this as soon as the health visitor walked through the door.

Although health visiting wasn't the most exciting of roles for a career nurse and adrenaline junkie like me, health visitors did sometimes have to deal with the most horrendous situations. They were often the first to pick up on suspected child abuse and became the villain in the eyes of the abusers for their part in involving social services and the law. Under child protection legislation, the health visitor was allowed – indeed, expected to breach confidentiality if they suspected abuse.

Student nurses are not taken into such households for two reasons. First, they would not be welcome, as often the health visitor wasn't welcome either, although on the whole, they were admitted. Second, the health visitor had to walk a thin line between trying to keep the family, including the suspected abuser, onside while reporting them. Dealing with students while this was all going on would be too much.

Chapter 13

Waterworks

A urology ward is all about internal plumbing and catheters, but as with any other ward, there can be poignant cases. Problems experienced by patients admitted to a urology ward are caused by some abnormality to the urethra or kidneys. These abnormalities can be strictures, where there is a narrowing of the urethra, or blockages, either benign or malignant, or infection.

I worked on a male urology ward where the majority of men came in for prostatectomy, removal of the prostate gland. The prostate gland could become cancerous or enlarged for other reasons, and when this happened, surgery was common. Post-op, the men had urinary catheters that were attached to bags, which were in turn attached to catheter stands at the side of their beds.

The prostate gland is vascular and there was always a lot of bloodied urine afterwards. The men were encouraged to drink plenty of water to clear out any clots and get the urine flowing properly again, but I recall one patient, Mr Fallon, refusing. We tried everything we could, explaining how important it was to keep drinking water and how his catheter could block or he might get an infection otherwise, but he was having none of it.

'Leave it to us, Nurse,' whispered Charlie, another patient, when I emptied his catheter bag while looking dolefully at Mr Fallon's small but bloody offering.

Later, when I came back from the sluice, I stared in disbelief at Mr Fallon's catheter bag. It was almost overflowing, as were those of the other six men in the bay.

'What the…?'

'We had a drinking competition, Nurse,' said Mr Fallon. 'And I won.'

Charlie winked at me as I quickly went off to collect more receptacles to empty all their bags.

Sometimes the camaraderie among patients was just as good as that among nurses and they often helped each other with recovery. They would cry on each other's shoulders, help each other eat, encourage each other in so many ways that I was often left as proud of them as a school teacher would be of their class or a mother of her children. Sadly, though, not every day was fun and not every patient recovered.

A twenty-eight-year-old man called Steve had been diagnosed with testicular cancer, which did seem to affect young men. He was soon to be wed when he was first diagnosed, then the worst news possible came back and the doctor had to tell him, his fiancée and his parents that his cancer was incurable.

His fiancée, Sian, was determined to go through with the wedding, and she and Steve were married shortly afterwards in the hospital chapel, with his family and as many of us nurses who could attend supporting them. I will never forget Steve, a strapping six-foot tall carpenter, who never made it home following his wedding. His new bride stayed by his side, laughing and joking with him until he died peacefully on the ward two days later. Afterwards, she was finally able to shed the tears that had never been far away, as were his parents.

Nowadays he would have survived, or at least had his life prolonged, and his sperm could have been added to a sperm bank should he and his wife have wanted to have children, but treatments were in their infancy and there was nothing anyone could do at that time.

It was always a privilege to care for people through their lowest times and an honour to look after people as brave as Steve, Sian and his parents, but it also took an emotional toll. The night Steve died, I split with my boyfriend. We rowed over something really stupid and I know it was because I was feeling raw and angry with the world, but my boyfriend just didn't care about the people I looked after.

'Why do you need to get involved? Cheer up, it's no-one we know.'

'But I *did* get to know him,' I answered. 'Can't you see? I'm not sad for me, I'm sad for his wife and his parents.'

'Are we going out or not?' had been the response.

'Not,' I answered and he'd left, slamming the door behind him. That night, I realised I could no sooner spend another day with this man than eat bulls' eyes. When he called the next day, I was not available. I cried all night, but not over my broken relationship; I cried for the many Steve's and Sian's I had met and cared for over the past five years. It was as though a dam had burst and I wept and wept until the next morning, when I got up, went to work and did it all over again because I loved my job.

Chapter 14

Respiratory

During my placement on a respiratory ward, quite a few patients with cystic fibrosis were admitted. Cystic fibrosis is a rare and life-limiting condition, and although life expectancy has improved since the 1980s, sufferers rarely make it into middle-age. The men and women who were admitted during my placement were often younger or not much older than myself.

The most common complication for patients who had cystic fibrosis was a chest infection. They required, and still do require, gruelling chest physiotherapy with postural drainage, which enabled them to cough up the infected green sputum which lingered on their lungs due to the lack of ciliary clearance, as well as other things. Antibiotic therapy was advancing, but was still limited and not always able to treat the infections as well back then. The patients might also have accompanying complications, one of which was diabetes mellitus due to the pancreas and digestive system not working properly.

Charlotte, a young woman I had cared for during numerous admissions to the ward, was one such person, and to make matters worse for her, she was on insulin. We had become friends, inasmuch as nurses became friends with patients; when someone is around your own age, sometimes professional barriers need to be broken down.

Charlotte was frequently admitted with rip-roaring chest infections, and on one such occasion, she asked for my telephone number and I gave it to her, even though it was not wise or even permitted to give patients your phone number then. One night, she called me out of the blue. I hadn't heard from her in months and had long since moved on from the respiratory ward.

'I've stopped taking my insulin.' She didn't sound very well at all and her speech was slurred.

'Charlotte, you can't do that, you could die.' There was no point beating about the bush.

'I don't care, I want to die.'

'Look, Charlotte, you have called me so I need to send an ambulance out to see you straight away. Do you understand?'

'Suppose so.' She put the phone down.

I called for an ambulance and gave them the address. The next day I checked admissions and, seeing where she was, I went to visit her.

She looked up sheepishly from her bed. 'Sorry.'

'That's alright, but don't ever do that again. I might not have been at home. What would you have done then?'

'I'm not sure,' she said as she picked at the bed sheets. 'Probably called Mum.'

'Thank goodness for that, but please don't do it again. If you're struggling, you need to see your consultant or ring the ward. You know they care about you, as does your mum.'

'I'm only delaying the inevitable, though, aren't I? I won't live much longer anyway.' She was right. It was only a matter of time and I had no idea how I would have coped with the condition back then when patients were lucky if they made it into their thirties.

That situation gave me a wake-up call on the dangers of giving patients my phone number. That said, I don't know what she would have done if she hadn't had the number. I told the staff nurse she was having morbid thoughts and she told me they had already referred her to the psychiatrist for assessment, as they did routinely if someone self-harmed.

I didn't hear from Charlotte again.

The respiratory ward was also a lifesaver for people with severe asthma attacks. A common treatment included salbutamol tablets, although they are no longer used for treatment of acute asthma now. Another treatment that remains true today was a salbutamol nebulise. An old-fashioned remedy that some nurses swore by was tincture of benzoin, which was administered via a Nelson's inhaler, named after the doctor who had invented it in the 1860s. Tincture of benzoin was no longer used in the 1980s, although we still used the Nelson's to administer menthol and steam inhalation for people with chronic bronchitis or sinusitis. The menthol would soothe the inflamed airways and the steam would loosen secretions so that patients could breathe more freely and cough up sticky sputum.

A regular attendee was admitted once again on her wedding night following another asthma attack. Her new husband appeared by her side, suitably alarmed and embarrassed, and we nurses ribbed him mercilessly once his bride had recovered. He blushed and explained it was due to the stress of the wedding day and nothing else. Needless to say, we didn't believe him.

Chapter 15

Nursing's Not for Everyone

The responsibilities of third-year students included training up the more junior students. There were numerous students on any one ward because, before Project 2000, students were part of the workforce and not extra-numerary. Teaching was fitted in among other ward duties and all of us had to take part, but training others was something I enjoyed, as I proved in later years when I taught both on the wards and in the classroom.

At one point during my training, I was moved back to a mixed surgical ward with twenty-six beds in a peripheral hospital to replace another third-year student who had been injured in a car accident and was not expected back for a few weeks. The ward included two side rooms and four six-bedded bays. On this particular day, I was allocated the right side of the ward; it was common practice at the time for one team to cover one side of the ward and another would cover the opposite side. Working alongside me was Gail, a first-year student nurse who was eight weeks into her first ward placement, Gwen, another first-year coming to the end of her placement, and a nursing auxiliary called Haley.

Surgical wards were always extremely busy with little or no let-up, and the term "deer in headlights" became a living reality that morning. Although I had no patients going for surgery, there were three patients for discharge and two due to be admitted to the ward. Gail appeared tense, but I remembered what it felt like to be a new student, so I tried to help her along a bit. She seemed keen to learn and did everything she was asked to do.

Breakfast was served to patients from a trolley wheeled on to the ward from the corridors leading to the bays and rooms. Gail was struggling to remember patients' names; in spite of being grilled to learn them ever since she'd started on the ward, she still didn't know who was in each room. Nowadays this is an all too common issue, but it was not acceptable when I trained. We had to know every patient's name and diagnosis by the end of a shift. Gail had been on the ward for eight weeks now so really needed to get a grip.

Once the breakfast round was finished, I left Gail and Haley to clear away dishes and make patient beds while Gwen and I sorted out the patients for discharge. When they'd made the beds, I asked Haley and Gail to help patients with personal hygiene. Haley had been on the ward for a few years, so was both adept and proficient at getting this job done. In the meantime, Gwen and I did wound checks and started an observation round.

After a couple of hours, it was time for breaks. I decided to take Gail with me, giving Haley a break as she was becoming impatient with the rather slow student. Gail was exceptionally quiet and it was difficult getting her to talk. After I'd persevered for a while, she finally spoke.

'I'm not sure nursing is for me. I freeze in front of patients,' she confided.

I felt sorry for her, but also felt she needed to lighten up, so I set myself the challenge of turning this situation around. She hadn't recognised the need to see the funny side of nursing and was taking herself and her job too seriously, which actually meant people weren't warming to her, and she in turn was clearly unhappy.

Once we got back to the ward, most of the morning jobs had been finished. Dr Curry arrived to write up the discharge medicines and Sister was in a mood. She was not at all impressed with the doctor as the medicines should have been prescribed the day before, but I shrugged my shoulders. At least they were done now.

I took Gail with me to the hospital pharmacy to get the drugs, explaining what each medicine was for and how important they were to the patients, but she really didn't seem to be with me. Her glazed look was becoming irritating, but I reminded myself what it was like to feel overwhelmed and persevered more slowly.

Relatives arrived on the ward and the discharged patients left. The new arrivals weren't in yet; they were due to arrive between 2 and 4 pm for surgery the next day. I took Gail on a round, going through each patient's name, what they were in for and how many days it would be until they were likely to be discharged, showing her how to go through observation and fluid charts as I did so.

At 11.30, we had a spare hour. Going into the treatment room, I asked Gail to run through a drip and she looked at me, not understanding what I had meant. I tried joking with her as I did with the patients during our round, but it was like pulling teeth. The patients had tried too, but she hadn't responded, so I thought a teaching session might help build her confidence.

'Well,' I explained, 'the new admissions will be going for surgery tomorrow and will need to have IV fluids, so you need to know how to set a drip up.'

In the middle of explaining how to carry out the procedure, which involved her running the intravenous fluid through a giving set that would then be attached to a cannula in the patient's arm, I suggested she attach the end of the giving set tube to my arm with tape. As she did so, I looked up as a visitor came in to ask how their family member was doing.

'Not you too, nurse!' they exclaimed, roaring with laughter. While I explained it was a teaching session and laughed with them, Gail didn't know where to look. I then went on to explain to Gail that on occasions, blood transfusions were necessary and proceeded to teach her about them, but soon realised this was a step too far.

After lunch, I went with Gail to admit one of the patients, explaining to the patient what the ward routine was, who would treat them and how the theatre list would be compiled later. It was a simple task: there were numerous questions on a page that I asked and the patient answered, then I told the patient I would let them know an approximate time for their operation or what number they were on the list as soon as I could. I then made observations, wrote them down on a chart, and we left.

This time, Gail seemed to get it, and I was struggling to understand why she hadn't known these things already when she had been on the ward for a couple of months. When I told her the next patient was hers, I don't think she believed me.

When the second patient came in, I handed Gail the admission pack, telling her to come back to me if she needed anything. I had no way of knowing that this simple instruction would be enough to send her into a full-blown panic attack.

Minutes later, she came back into the treatment room, unable to speak, gasping for breath. I grabbed a paper bag, thankful that a lot of equipment came in paper bags, and managed to put it over her mouth and nose, telling her to slow her breathing down.

At last, she seemed to calm down, but it took an age. Sister came in to the treatment room, demanding to know what had gone on. I explained that I had done an admission with Gail this afternoon, and had then asked her to do a second. Sister nodded, clearly understanding.

'Nurse Prentice, go to the kitchen and make yourself a cup of tea. I will see you in a minute.'

Gail, who had recovered from her shock and panic attack, quickly left the room.

'This is unfortunate, Nurse Brookes, but I fear Nurse Prentice is just not cut out for nursing. She has been here for several weeks now and has not been able to do much at all. Even taking temperatures at times seems to be too much trouble. The other nurses have had enough and, quite frankly, so have I. Nursing's not for everyone. Please admit the second patient yourself and I will speak to Nurse Prentice. I'll see if I can find out what's going on.'

'Yes, Sister,' I replied, completely flabbergasted by Gail's lack of ability to ask a set of simple questions and feeling a little bit guilty at having allocated her the job in the first place.

I saw Gail enter Sister's office rather sheepishly. Later, Sister let me know Gail had some personal health issues and would pause her training to restart again in six months, but she didn't give me any details. In the meantime, Gail was going off duty and would be on sick leave.

My chin hit the floor. What had I done? It was a heavy burden to bear, feeling responsible for a colleague's downfall. I struggled to work to the end of that shift, and in the end, Sister called me into the office.

'Put this behind you, Nurse, it was not your fault. If it hadn't been you, it would have been someone else. The senior nursing officer has been aware, almost from the outset, that there was a situation here. Has the rest of the work been done?'

'Yes, Sister,' I replied.

'Okay, Nurse Brookes, just write up the notes ready for handover. That's all.'

I did as I was told, realising that what Sister had said was true, but still feeling sorry it had been me who sent the poor girl into a panic.

It turned out Sister was having a bad day that day; they do happen. Another incident had occurred involving a work-experience schoolgirl who had been helping out to see how a hospital ward ran. Sister had explained that some of the patients were unable to eat or drink due to their surgery that morning, hence very large signs above the beds stating: NIL BY MOUTH. A nursing auxiliary had done the first round with the young girl, giving out tea and coffee. The next round, the young girl felt sure she could manage it herself and the auxiliary let her.

Sister was doing her round a bit later than usual, given what she called the "Prentice situation", and unfortunately – or fortunately, depending on your viewpoint – she went in to see one of the patients who was due to have surgery within the hour, only to find her tucking into tea and cake.

'Cake's lovely, Sister, are they home-made?'

'No, they are bought in, but you do realise you're due for surgery any minute, Mrs Knowles?'

'Am I?' she exclaimed. 'What for?'

'You've come in to have your gallbladder out.'

'Really? Well I never!'

Sister looked at the observation chart and noted that the patient had a temperature of 39°C, but no-one had acted on it. Calling the senior student, Sarah, into the office, she asked her to explain. Sarah was unable to do so as she hadn't known about it. Her first-year student, Brendon, had done the observations and not reported back to her.

'You're responsibility, Nurse, not his.'

Poor Sarah, I did feel for her.

'Follow me.' Sister led her to the ward desk. 'Here's the phone, Nurse. You need to phone Dr Curry, tell him what's happened and get him to the ward – now!'

As Sarah grappled with the phone, Sister left her to it. Sarah then had to discuss with Brendon the importance of not just doing observations, but acting on the results.

Dr Curry appeared on the ward and was told about the patient's high temperature and the tea and cake fiasco. He went and examined the patient and diagnosed a chest infection, explaining that surgery would not be suitable that day, then left to inform the consultant and the theatre team, kindly leaving out the fact that the patient had eaten. The surgery would have had to be cancelled anyway, even if the volunteer schoolgirl hadn't given food and drink to the elderly woman. The girl had no understanding of the impact of what she had done and Sister decided not to tell her. She was, however, never left to do rounds alone again.

Chapter 16

Breaking the Rules

Sometimes nurses broke rules for their own personal gain, such as sneaking men into their rooms in the nurses' home or food from the food trolley into the kitchen on a late shift. I was as guilty as anyone of breaking these rules, particularly the latter when my overdraft was so large I was living on fresh air, justifying my actions by telling myself that the food would most likely be thrown away when it was returned to the kitchens. I *never* took food from a trolley until all the patients had been fed. This was in the days before outside caterers were involved in providing hospital food. To be honest, I don't think I would ever have stolen what they serve up as an excuse for food, but that's a different story.

Another absolute no-no was to become romantically involved with a patient, although some nurses crossed this line too. It was difficult at times for young nurses, who were wooed by patients of both sexes, to resist, and even some doctors could fall foul of this rule. There were many other rules, some sensible and some ridiculous, that we broke on a daily basis, and I will now confess to a couple of instances where I broke hospital rules.

Bill was a tramp – a commonly used term in the early 1980s for a homeless person – who was admitted to the surgical ward one day when we were on take, meaning we took emergency admissions via casualty and the community. I wondered why the ambulance crew thrust a folder into my hands, and then did a *Roadrunner* impression – I couldn't see them for dust as they left the ward.

Making my way towards the closed curtains, I soon smelled why they had left in such a hurry. I cautiously opened the curtains to find a man who looked like he was in his eighties, but was in fact only sixty-seven, sitting in the wheelchair that had been abandoned by the ambulance crew when they'd left the ward, telling him they had to dash off to an emergency. I glanced quickly at his folder and the ambulance crew's report.

William Yates, the record said, had been found under a bridge with bleeding to his head. A concerned member of the public had called for an ambulance. As I scanned down the notes, I found the casualty record was sparse.

Admit surgical ward for assessment by on-call SHO later. This was doctor speak for "We don't want him in casualty and no doctor is going to examine him until he's been cleaned up by a nurse."

I could see some old dried blood beneath cakes of dirt on the elderly man's forehead, but it was everything else that I saw that concerned me. His eyes had sunk into his skull; his once red beard, now black, and the multiple marks to his face and hands told me he was not the only admission. He had brought an army of little friends with him.

'Mr Yates, my name is Nurse Brookes. Would you mind if I took you to the bathroom so that I can help you change into some hospital pyjamas?'

'Name's Bill. Do what you want, but don't take me bag.'

He was hanging on tightly to an old sack – containing whisky, I suspected – but first things first. I called Tracy, a second-year student, and asked her to fill a bath and add cetrimide, a skin disinfectant, to the water. The smell told her the reason for my request and she shrugged her shoulders before dutifully heading towards the bathroom. I wheeled the chair from the side of the bed, already noticing a few escapees on the floor. As I headed towards the bathroom, I saw the ward domestic charge behind the curtains to start her scrubbing, and noticed that the rest of the ward staff and patients gave me a wide berth.

Sister scowled, not happy that this man had not been "cleaned up" before arriving on a surgical ward. She ran a tight ship and bacteria, let alone the goodies Bill had brought with him, were absolutely forbidden.

The bathwater was a lovely bright yellow and the smell of disinfectant almost helped to mask the odours emanating from Bill. The elderly man looked frail and was clearly tired, so didn't give us much in the way of assistance – or resistance, thankfully. Having donned gloves and aprons, we began the task of removing Bill's clothes. The threadbare coat was first off and Tracy held open a red linen bag to receive it. Red linen bags were for clothing and bed linen that was destined for incineration, and these clothes had only one destination in my opinion.

'Check the pockets,' I said to Tracy, who screwed her nose up at the thought while Bill sat dozing in the wheelchair. There were a few coins and an almost empty whisky bottle, along with a handful of mints that had turned black and one cigarette. The whisky bottle and the mints went in the bin and the coat finally made it into the waiting laundry bag.

With each layer of clothes that came off, there was more movement as fleas and lice made their escape. Finally, all the clothes were in the incinerator and all Bill's "worldly goods" sat on a shelf. These consisted of a few coins, an old penknife and a photo of a young couple on their wedding day.

Bill had woken by now and was looking suspiciously towards the bath. His body, still crawling with fleas, was red raw from bites and scratches.

'Don't worry, Bill. We'll help you in and then get you into a hospital gown.'

In spite of his emaciated frame, Bill managed to get into the bath with a minimum of assistance. The water was blackened almost immediately and the fleas that had managed to stay on his body floated dead in the water. Tracy washed his body while I secured the laundry bag so that none of the contents would be able to escape, sprinkling the top of the bag with a disinfectant that would kill any that did make it out. We emptied and refilled the bath while Bill was still inside and began work on his hair and beard.

'Do you mind if we get rid of the beard, Bill?' I asked. 'I want to see that handsome face underneath.'

He grinned a cigarette-stained grin, showing the few teeth that remained in his mouth, and his deep-set eyes finally smiled.

'Go on, then. Ya might as well, seeing as you've already got rid of all me clothes.'

A yellow plastic bag – again for incineration – was made ready to receive the hair from the beard as I began cutting it away to make way for shaving. I was trying to ignore the head lice that crawled around inside the matted hair and beard. As soon as I finished cutting the beard, Tracy filled Bill's chin and upper lip with shaving foam while I started on the equally matted hair that was down to his shoulders.

Once we had finished, the bath was littered with dead lice, so we emptied and refilled it for a third time. Next we applied head lice shampoo to his hair to kill off any remaining marauders. We washed Bill's skin gently and, once he was out of the bath, helped dry him.

As I dried his hands and feet, between the webs of his fingers and toes, I noticed the familiar tracks of scabies. I sighed heavily and pulled a bottle of treatment out of the cupboard. Bill was finally shiny clean and almost handsome as his aquiline nose was now visible.

'How do you feel?' I asked him.

'Terrible,' he answered. 'Where's my bag?'

I had removed a full bottle of whisky from the sackcloth and put it to one side. 'Sorry, Bill, I had to throw the bag out, but the whisky will be locked away until you're discharged.'

He grunted with disgust. 'Well that better be soon,' he snorted.

I took Bill back to the bed that he had been allocated while Tracy cleared up the bathroom. Sister was still glowering as I went past. It wasn't as if it was my fault, but that made no difference to her and she gave me a hard time all shift.

Bill only stayed for two days as there was nothing really wrong with him that warranted a surgical admission. The bleeding had been due to his scratching away at the infestation that blighted him. The social worker arranged for him to be discharged to a hostel.

'I ain't staying in no hostel. What do you think I am? I've got me pride, you know.'

'Well you can't keep living under a bridge, can you?' I retorted. We had developed an understanding and I'd grown fond of the belligerent Bill Yates. 'Anyway, now you're leaving us, are you going to tell me who's in that photo?' I'd been asking him for days, but he would just tap his finger on his nose to tell me to mind my own business.

He sighed. 'She was me wife.' He stroked the picture. 'That's us on our wedding day. She went to Holland during the war to find out if her family was alright. I was in the RAF and serving overseas or I never would have let her go.'

He bowed his head and mumbled the next few words.

'I returned home after the war to find she'd never come back.'

Tears fell down Bill's face. He looked up, sniffed, and then shook himself. 'Anyway, that was a long time ago, don't matter now.' He took the bottle of whisky and his photo and walked off the ward. I stared after him, tears falling down my face too.

Bill returned to his "home" under the bridge and I visited him most weeks, taking him to the hospital when I knew it was quiet for a weekly bath. Strictly forbidden, of course, but this was one of the rules that was meant to be broken.

Eventually, the social worker and I managed to get him ensconced in a small council flat with meals on wheels. The last time I saw him, he was living in a rather untidy flat, but at least it was warm. He was still getting his weekly bath, but this time it was arranged legitimately by social services.

I often wonder what happened to Bill and am always grateful to the servicemen and women who fought for our freedom during both world wars. He reminded me that many of them returned to find that home wasn't the way they had left it.

While I was working on the surgical ward in the peripheral hospital, Ray was admitted. A thirty-two-year-old alcoholic who also lived rough, Ray had been admitted to the medical ward first with pneumonia, but was transferred to the surgical ward for insertion of bands for oesophageal varices.

Alcohol abuse often results in huge varicose veins around the oesophagus, and if these burst – I have seen this happen once – the patient vomits copious amounts of blood and dies almost immediately. Banding is used to prevent the varices from bursting, but there is still a risk of more developing if the person continues to drink, which more often than not, they do.

I hadn't actually had much to do with Ray, apart from a brief conversation while I was checking his obs, and he was discharged when I was on a late shift. On finishing my shift, I walked along the corridor towards the changing room and heard a noise coming from inside the chapel. I looked inside and saw Ray sitting on the front row, crying. I couldn't leave him there this late at night, so I walked in and sat next to him.

'Are you okay?' I asked – stupid question as he clearly was not.

'I don't want to drink anymore, but I can't stop. If I go back to the hostel where I was, I'll just start again, I know I will.'

I sat quietly, waiting for him to continue.

'What will you do?' I asked finally.

'I don't know. Are you a Christian?'

'Yes, I am. Are you looking for someone to pray with you?'

Strictly speaking, I was not breaking any rules as I wasn't proselytising a patient. I'd found him in the chapel and assumed he had entered for a reason, and I was off duty so I offered to pray with him – not something I did every day.

'Would you pray for me now?'

I did pray. I asked God to help him overcome his problem with drinking. Then I had an idea.

'Why don't I take you to the YMCA? It's on my way home.'

He nodded and agreed to wait while I went and changed. I took him to the YMCA and paid for him to stay the first couple of nights, then I left him to it.

Nine months later, I received a phone call. I had been living in a bedsit for almost a year and now had a phone.

'It's Ray.'

At first I didn't have a clue who Ray was and must have sounded suitably confused.

'Ray from the hospital chapel. You took me to the YMCA.'

The voice on the other end of the phone was a far cry from the dejected voice of the man in the chapel.

'Ray! How are you?'

'Thanks to you, I'm great. I turned my life around, got a job and haven't touched the drink since we met.'

'Wow, that's brilliant.' I was delighted, but a bit hesitant, hoping the next sentence wasn't going to involve asking me for a date.

'I phoned because I needed to tell you something. You gave the YMCA your phone number when you left me there.'

That answered my unspoken question as to how he had my number.

'Anyway, I hung on to it until I felt that I was really making a clean break from the booze. That night in the chapel, before you came along, I prayed. I told God I wanted to give up the drink, and that if He really existed and gave a toss, He'd send someone to help me to prove it. Almost as soon as I finished that prayer, you sat next to me. I just wanted to tell you that you were the answer to my prayer that day. Now I'm happy, I've got a steady job and go to church.'

'Thanks for letting me know. I'm really pleased for you, Ray.'

'I'll always be grateful to you, and to God.'

We said our goodbyes and he hung up. I was left in awe. Reflecting on that evening nine months ago, I hoped that if the same thing happened again, I would behave in exactly the same way, even if it meant blurring the boundaries.

Chapter 17

Down, but Not Out

Sometimes it's difficult to remember that nurses and doctors are human too. They suffer heartbreak, ill health, depression, and some even die young like those they care for. But being young and in the health profession, we student nurses often felt we were invincible. Occasionally we would be reminded that there is no such thing.

One of the saddest times of my training years came when a friend was diagnosed with lymphoma. Mark was just twenty-eight and loved life. We had got to know each other at church and were always talking and laughing together. We would cook for each other and he introduced me to Ethiopian food. I often teased him that he ate too much meat, and he teased me back that people frequently ate raw meat at home.

Then Mark started to lose weight and had some bowel symptoms that he wouldn't discuss with me. He looked pale. It was obvious to me, having nursed so many patients with cancer, that something was seriously wrong, but I hoped it was something less dangerous.

One night he was admitted to hospital with severe abdominal pain and an emergency laparotomy (opening of the abdomen) was carried out to relieve a blockage. A week later he was diagnosed with lymphoma and told that his condition was inoperable and untreatable.

I visited Mark in a home where he was being looked after by a couple from the church and watched him waste away and die within a few weeks of diagnosis. I found it doubly difficult as I was working on a male medical ward at the time where there were numerous patients with terminal cancer. Caring for people all day and watching a close friend fade away at night was taking its toll and I was feeling like a miserable wreck.

It was one of the most difficult times in my nursing career and I struggled to be the happy but compassionate nurse I usually was when on the ward. I was emotionally drained after Mark died, but I had to struggle in to work each day as if nothing had happened. We were not allowed time off for bereavement except in the case of close family, and the reality hit me one night that Mark and I had had a friendship that most probably would have developed into a relationship had he not become ill.

I did manage to request a day off for the funeral by changing shifts with a friend who knew about Mark. The day of the funeral came and his family had flown over from Ethiopia. Mark's body lay in an open coffin, as was the tradition of the orthodox church of Ethiopia to which his family belonged.

The hardest part for me was at the graveside. As the coffin was lowered into the ground, the family began wailing loudly and shaking incense balls. The latter I didn't mind, but the wailing was something I had never experienced, and is not something I would ever wish to experience again. And believe me, I was wailing inside. I was impatient with this outward display of emotion, but realised later that it was traditional for his culture. Almost as soon as the screaming and crying had started, it stopped again when the ceremony was considered over.

There was a dinner afterwards for the hundreds of people who had attended the funeral. Mark had become very popular within a short space of time and I will always remember the conversations we had, the mealtimes we shared, and that his life was far too short.

Ginny was one of the girls I had got to know through our training. She was a couple of years younger than me, but we got on well, often joking around in class when the tutors were trying to teach us something serious. It was our way of handling the pressures of learning anatomy and physiology while working like Trojans on the wards. Ginny and I almost always sat together in class.

We were in a two-week block of classroom teaching when I noticed something wasn't right. One morning, about a week in, I handed Ginny a drink at lunchtime. She took the drink and dropped it, spilling coffee all over the place. As she swore loudly, people turned their heads to see what was going on.

'Don't worry,' I said. 'I'll get some paper towels and clear it up, then I'll get you another one.' Ginny just stared down at the floor where the spilled coffee was pooling.

After I'd bought the second drink, I placed it on the coffee table in front of her. I was worried; I'd noticed she was becoming a bit vacant at times and very clumsy, but each time I asked if everything was okay, she said it was.

'What is it, Ginny?' I asked as I sat next to her.

'I'm not sure, I keep dropping things and yesterday I fell over. I think I'm just tired. You know what it's like – we work too hard and I've been studying night and day to get ready for finals.'

'That's probably it, Ginny, but have you thought about seeing a doctor?'

'What, and be called a neurotic nurse?' she exclaimed.

She had a point; it's difficult when you work in the health profession to strike a balance between neurosis and dismissiveness. Every ache or pain could be interpreted as a sign of some incurable disease, every symptom serious and every tear a breakdown. Some medical professionals develop a condition known as Munchausen's Disease where they imagine symptoms and spend their lives visiting doctors, even having unnecessary surgery. Others dismiss every symptom as nothing, not wanting to be labelled the neurotic nurse, and rarely go to see a doctor. Occasionally, they leave seeking help too late.

Ginny's symptoms were not imaginary, and if I had noticed them, things were clearly not right.

'I wouldn't worry about that. You never go to the doctor, so in your case the label won't apply. It might be worth going, just for a check-up and a bit of reassurance if necessary.'

'I'll think about it.'

Ginny didn't go to the doctor, and a few weeks later, she fell during a shift on the surgical ward where she was working. Only this time, she couldn't get herself up. She was whisked away to occupational health and referred urgently for a neurological assessment.

A few weeks later, I went to visit her in the nurses' home and she told me she'd been diagnosed with Multiple Sclerosis, a condition that consisted of relapses and remissions leading to disability, the severity of which depended on how bad the condition was.

'I've had to give up, Dawn. I won't be sitting finals. We can't have an invalid working on the wards, can we? That's what the senior nurse told the head tutor.'

I didn't know what to say. Ginny had wanted to become a nurse since she was playing with her first doll, whereas I'd just sleepwalked into the profession. I was gutted for her.

We said our goodbyes and Ginny's parents collected her later that day to return to Bournemouth where they lived. For a while after that, I felt like a neurotic nurse myself, but managed to get things back into perspective after a few weeks on the wards. After all, I had finals to study for.

I met Cameron when I worked at the peripheral hospital. As a pharmacist, he visited the ward daily, went through all the patients' drug charts and checked the ward stocks. We would always chat when he came along and he seemed to linger on our ward.

One of my new nurse friends was a charismatic girl called Rowena who invited me to the Christian Union she'd set up at the hospital. I was delighted to see Cameron there when I attended the first meeting. It was a fun time where, as well as Bible study, we played games, ate food and got to know each other.

Rowena was dating a guy from her church, but they were having difficulties with their parents. Rowena was black while Alan was white. In fact, he couldn't have been whiter with very pale skin and blond hair, whereas Rowena couldn't have been much darker in terms of skin colour.

The time came when they wanted to get married, but both sets of parents were refusing permission on the grounds of race. They could have married anyway because they were both old enough, but they wanted their families' blessing and both sets of parents had reached an impasse.

Meanwhile, Cameron and I were getting to know each other better, and we would have the occasional night out as a foursome with Rowena and Alan. I felt sorry for them, but they remained bubbly and happy, determined to bring their parents round to accepting their choice of marriage partner.

The opportunity came for Rowena when Alan's mum was taken ill and had to have surgery. His dad had to keep working and they were struggling. Every day, before and after work,

Rowena would visit Alan's home and cook for his mum. At first, Alan's mum would refuse to eat the food, but Rowena kept visiting anyway. She also cleaned and shopped for them while Alan's mum recovered.

One day, Rowena went to visit when Alan's mum and dad were both at home.

'Alright, you can marry our son,' his mum said, smiling. After that, there were never any issues of race from Alan's family.

'One down, one to go,' Rowena told us at the CU meeting. 'This is the hardest part, though. My dad insists that "no white man will ever be part of his family".' We laughed as she mimicked her father's voice.

'What are you going to do?' asked Cameron.

'Alan and I are going to Rwanda for a fortnight next month.'

'But I thought you said your dad wouldn't let him visit?' I said.

'I managed to get the village elder to give permission. Dad would never go against the village elder.'

'What, for the marriage?' I asked.

'No, just for the visit. He won't interfere on the marriage front.'

Six weeks later, Rowena and Alan were engaged to be married. When we asked how Alan had managed to get her father's permission, she told us how he had visited her father every day, sat down on the floor with him, eaten things with his hands that he had never eaten in his life, and joined in all the village activities. At first, her father wouldn't even acknowledge Alan, but after a while he won over her mum, and once that battle had been won, victory in the war would inevitably follow.

'My dad thinks he rules the roost, but without my mum, he wouldn't eat! Besides, even my dad agreed in the end that Alan was as good as any black man he had ever met.'

The happy couple were married in the summer and moved to Wales shortly afterwards to go to Bible College before working abroad.

Cameron and I couldn't quite follow this love story. Although we did become romantically involved for a while, there just wasn't the spark. I felt like we were going through the motions and had been better friends than we were a couple.

With a heavy heart, I ended our relationship and Cameron married another nurse a year later. I was sad for a short time and wondered if I had made the wrong decision, but the busyness of the day job took over and I threw all my energies into that, remembering to leave my problems at the door.

Chapter 18

Pride Comes Before a Fall

The junior house officers (JHOs) had only been working on the wards for eight weeks, but sometimes you would have thought they were superior beings as they donned their white coats and paraded around as if they owned the hospital. The white coats flapped as they wandered through the corridors with the *British National Formulary* stuffed into their pockets and stethoscopes around their necks. Some of them were great, others were lucky the stethoscope wasn't used to strangle them.

The senior house officers (SHOs) were not around so much when the juniors appeared on the wards, leaving them to manage unsupervised, and most of them did manage – most of the time. After all, the tasks they were given back then would now mostly be carried out by nurses.

As a third-year student nurse, I had enough to think about seeing to patients without having to watch JHOs with a superiority complex swanning around. I remember one particular ward, a female surgical ward, had twenty-eight beds and was busy all the time. Patients generally stayed on the ward for around ten days, and admissions and discharges had to be managed in a timely fashion.

But one day was an exception to this rule and the ward was unusually quiet. I was on a late shift and started at 12.30pm. After the handover, there was not a lot to do.

Sister told me to use the time wisely and take the opportunity to teach one of the junior students. This was to help prepare me for my forthcoming management assessment. On my management assessment day, I would have to run the ward, but I would also have to teach. Today, I would be part of the team that sat at the nurses' station and delegated work for a change.

The phone rang. Usually the senior nurse would answer it, but Sister looked at me.

'Go on, Nurse Brookes, answer the phone and deal with whatever it is.'

'Yes, Sister,' I replied as I took the call. 'Benson Ward, Nurse Brookes speaking.'

'Staff Nurse Jacobs in casualty here. Have you got a bed for a forty-seven-year-old woman with abdominal pain?' Knowing how many empty beds there were on the ward was important as casualty staff would expect swift transfers of patients.

'Yes, we can take her, what's the diagnosis?'

'SHO thinks she's got ulcerative colitis. Currently dehydrated and in a lot of pain. Intramuscular meds written up, she's had some metoclopramide and is on an IV drip. She'll be with you in the next half-hour.'

'Okay,' I said and put the phone down.

'Well,' said Sister, 'What's happening?'

I repeated the information and suggested that my student could prepare the bed for the patient and together we would admit her.

'Very well, Nurse.'

That seemed to be that. I went out to the ward to find the first-year student nurse, Rose, to explain what was happening. The patient duly arrived and was settled into a bed. We checked her blood pressure, pulse, temperature and respiratory rate, requested she provide a urine sample and took down details for our nursing notes. Once she was admitted, I went to phone the JHO on call to get him to come to the ward to clerk her in.

Dr Baines was one of the most arrogant house officers I had come across. He was around my age, but there the similarity ended. He was always in a hurry, always abrupt, and rarely deigned to lower himself enough to acknowledge any of the nurses, except for Sister.

He arrived on the ward after an hour and asked where the patient he was to clerk was. I noticed he was unusually sombre and his porcelain-like skin was red from the neck up; he was clearly embarrassed about something. I asked the most junior nurse available to accompany him behind the curtains. Usually I would have taken pleasure in this, knowing it would annoy him, but on this day he accepted everything without comment.

Something had obviously happened to him and I was intrigued as to what had caused this change in his behaviour. He wasn't friendly by any means, but he was certainly subdued and not his usual obnoxious self.

Sister and a second-year student left the ward for their evening dinner break. While they were gone, I was in Sister's office, writing up the nursing notes and night report as part of my management preparation. Dr Baines came in and coughed sheepishly before explaining the treatment he was recommending for our new patient. Curiosity was killing me now as I looked at this difficult man who, at that moment, looked like a child about to cry.

'Are you alright?' I asked, knowing full well he wasn't. 'You seem upset. Has something happened to you?'

He threw himself down in the chair opposite Sister's desk and sighed.

'I've made a bit of a balls up and am in the doghouse.'

'What did you do?'

'I clerked a patient in on Taylor ward. He had severe abdominal pain. I prescribed intramuscular analgesia, told him he had appendicitis and that he would need surgery tonight.'

'Okay, following you so far. What was wrong with that?' I was puzzled because it all sounded reasonable and his SHO would have approved his decision. 'Was it the wrong diagnosis?'

'No, it was the right diagnosis. I told the patient what would happen next,' he said.

I was still confused. Nothing he'd said so far seemed wrong and the patient needed to know what was going to happen to him.

'I told the patient, which was fine. He had had surgery before so knew the nurses should be coming to get him ready, but nothing had happened so he asked the staff nurse why because he was still in agony. She told him that as far as she knew, he wasn't going to theatre. The ward sister read my notes and then called me. I got a blasting for not telling the nurses about surgery, and she wanted to know why I thought that she had psychic powers that would tell her when someone was going to theatre.'

Stifling a giggle, I encouraged him to go on. I knew I shouldn't be, but I was enjoying this.

'So the patient wasn't prepped. I then got it in the neck from the theatre sister because they hadn't set up for surgery. Then the anaesthetist shouted at me as there could be no anaesthetic without him. Finally, the SHO yelled at me because I hadn't told him and he'd been told off by the registrar because I was his responsibility. He told me that without a surgeon, there could be no op. Then he told me my communication skills were appalling and went into a tirade about all the complaints he was getting from ward staff about my behaviour.'

'Really?' I couldn't help myself. As much as I had sympathy for him, I just had to laugh. It was too difficult to contain. Eventually, he saw the funny side too. He had learned a hard lesson that day. Had he been a bit nicer, he would have still been in trouble, but not quite as much as he had experienced.

It was always a pleasure when an arrogant doctor or nurse was pulled down a peg or two.

One of the student nurses in the set, Wilma, seemed to have a chip on her shoulder. Nothing was ever right and she was constantly complaining that she was passed over for the nicer jobs on the wards.

'I'm just as good as everyone else. What's the matter with them?' By 'them' she meant the senior ward staff.

There was no doubt that she was intelligent and would be able to pass the written examinations. The truth was that there were doubts about her practical skills and her attitude, both of which she would require when she became a staff nurse.

I happened to be working on the same ward as Wilma and found myself on the same shift. I was preparing five patients for theatre, administering pre-meds, along with helping the staff nurse do the medicine round. I was also delegating work to the nursing auxiliary and a first-year student, who were making beds and giving out breakfasts.

I went to break with Gracie, the first year. On our arrival back on the ward, we saw our staff nurse talking to the other staff nurse, who was working the early shift. It was a little odd as it wasn't patient mealtime or handover and there was still a mountain of jobs to get through before lunchtime.

Wilma, looking rather sheepish, was then led into the treatment room by the staff nurses. I wondered what was going on. The next thing I knew, the JHO was called to the ward and the staff nurses went with him in to Sister's office. Wilma was left standing in the treatment room, so I asked her if everything was alright

She stared at me. I wasn't sure whether she was upset, angry or a mix of both.

'What's happened?' I asked.

'I'm just as capable of giving injections as you or anyone else on this ward,' she snarled. 'There were two left to be given, one to Mrs Smith and one to Miss Finch. Knowing I would not be trusted to give or check the injection, I picked one of them up and gave it to Miss Finch. Unfortunately, it was morphine that should have been given to Mrs Smith. Now the JHO is up to sort out this mess which wouldn't have happened if they had bothered to include me in the first place. It's their fault, not mine.'

Her face was beetroot red and she stormed off, back on to the ward. How do you deal with someone like that? I was glad this wasn't my management assessment day or it would have been left to me to sort it out.

Miss Finch was assessed by the JHO and was no worse off for the error, but it could have been much more serious had it been a different drug. The staff nurses were also at fault as controlled drugs should not have been drawn up and left unattended in the treatment room, not that it would have stopped my irresponsible colleague, who should have checked the charts and been accompanied by a qualified staff member anyway.

I knew heads would roll and was glad to get back to my side of the ward.

The staff nurses were disciplined and received warnings, and they had to be retrained in the handling of controlled drugs. Wilma was severely reprimanded and failed her ward placement as well as receiving a verbal warning. She later failed her drugs assessment and decided to jump before she was pushed. A decision, in my opinion, that improved the safety of patients everywhere.

Chapter 19

Management Assessment

The day of my management assessment arrived. I didn't know why I was so nervous as I'd managed wards as an enrolled nurse and on night shifts; it's something about having your every move watched that sends shivers down the spine.

I had to wait fretfully through the morning as I was on a late shift. I would be watched for the first half of the shift, so it was by far the hardest assessment other than finals. Waking early, I went for a three-mile jog then showered, changed and had breakfast. I tried to study, but nothing was going in; I just had to wait it out.

I knew the patients on the ward well. The consultant would be doing a round, which I hated, but it was all part of the job so wouldn't be too onerous.

When I arrived on the ward fifteen minutes early, Sister greeted me.

'Nervous, Nurse Brookes? Surely not. No need, you will pass with flying colours. Just keep your head when all around are losing theirs.' She chuckled at her joke.

I listened intently to the handover. Did I hear everything? Did my notes tell me everything I had to do? Taking a deep breath, I headed out to the ward with the clinical tutor who would be assessing me in tow.

Heather, a second-year student, would be my support. I knew she was good so had no worries about her ability. We went around the ward and checked patient charts; I had to verbalise everything I was doing to the tutor so that she knew I understood. I checked that observations and drips were up-to-date and requested changes where they were needed, then checked on the patients who were due for discharge.

One patient was for transfer to another hospital nearer home, and three were for complete discharge. It would be a busy shift as the morning staff had left everything for me, as was often the case when someone was doing a management assessment. The JHO had written up discharge medicines and letters, so I was grateful for that.

Heather and I sorted out the patients for discharge, cleaned the rooms, made the beds and did obs on the rest of the patients. The great thing about doing a management assessment was that I got to delegate work to the ward sister and I had given her one side of the ward to look after, while Heather and I took the other.

The consultant, Mr Hart, arrived for his round at two-thirty and Sister grabbed him on his way in to tell him I was doing my management assessment. Patients and staff closed ranks whenever a nurse was doing an assessment – it was wink-wink, nod-nod as we headed off on the round. I wasn't sure if Mr Hart would be better or worse than normal, but hopefully Sister had warned him to go easy – especially if he wanted his tea and cake at the end of the round.

It was going well until we came to Mrs Beck, an eighty-year-old lady who had had surgery, but was at risk of developing pressure sores. As the consultant went to examine her, the bootees that she had been wearing on her ankles were in the bed. Sister apologised to the consultant for the mishap.

'Nurse Brookes, you really must manage patient care better,' she snapped. So much for the consultant going easy; Sister had temporarily lost it, while Mr Hart didn't seem at all concerned. At least the observations were up to date.

The round continued uneventfully, then I answered the office phone to a nurse from casualty.

'We need to send a female patient to you, she has appendicitis and may need surgery. Another one is coming to you with cholecystitis, should be with you within the hour.'

As I took the details and thanked the nurse before putting the receiver down, I could hear the clicking of Sister's heels approaching. Why did she have to wear loud heels today, of all days? Normally they were quiet. Perhaps she wanted me to know she was coming.

'Nurse Brookes, when are you planning to do your teaching session?' What a time to ask. Gathering my thoughts, I looked sheepishly at the clinical tutor, who silently continued writing notes.

'About 4pm,' I answered. 'I will be teaching the first years how to admit a patient to a surgical ward and what they need to know regarding an individual patient's surgery. There's a patient coming in later for drainage of a pilonidal sinus tomorrow. I thought that might be appropriate.'

'Okay, Nurse, I'll get back to my work then.'

I looked at the clock and realised it was time for break, so I asked a staff nurse to cover my patients while Heather and I went. Thankfully, the clinical tutor didn't accompany us so I got half an hour to de-stress.

When I got back, the two new patients had arrived from casualty. I had to assess who should be seen first. The patient with cholecystitis had been given buscopan, an anti-spasmodic, and morphine and was settled, but the appendicitis patient was in pain. I asked Heather to admit that patient first while I bleeped the JHO to let him know the patients had arrived and that the appendicitis patient was in pain.

Sister must have overheard me speaking to the doctor because she was on my heels.

'Nurse Brookes, are you going to let theatre know? Is the JHO on his way? What medication has the patient been given and why? Is it enough? Think, Nurse, this patient needs you now. What are you going to do?'

I had felt fully in control of the situation, but now my head was spinning. I went into the office to get notes ready and thankfully the clinical tutor didn't follow me. By then the JHO had arrived and asked why I was in a quandary.

'Don't worry,' he said when I explained. 'She's not going to theatre now. That's my decision, not hers. Sister's testing you, trying to make you panic to see how you'll react when everyone around you is stressed. Stay strong.'

I remembered Sister's words from earlier and now her harassment made sense.

Sister and the clinical tutor came at me again. This time I was prepared. 'No decision has been made to take this patient to theatre as yet,' I heard myself say in a quiet, calm voice. 'Therefore she will be assessed by the JHO and I will monitor her condition and inform the JHO of any changes. In the meantime, the patient with cholecystitis also needs my attention as she has a fever. Her temperature is 39°C. I need to go and see her.'

I walked out looking calmer than I felt with palpations in my chest following my near-miss. Somehow, I had to keep my cool; I did not want to fail the assessment and have a repeat of this.

Once the ward was in order, and Heather and I had given appropriate treatment to the new admissions, I took the first-year students to the patient who was due for surgery tomorrow for the teaching session. At 5pm, Sister called me into the office.

'Just a few questions, Nurse Brookes.' For another hour, I was grilled on every subject common to the surgical ward, as well as some complicated issues such as complaints from patients and junior staff. She asked me about the medicines used and what side effects might be experienced by patients to ensure I knew all about these. We discussed surgical procedures and I felt like I had been dissected by the end of the hour. Sister and the clinical tutor then dismissed me and stayed in the office before calling me back half an hour later.

I had passed my assessment.

I went out to tell the staff nurse and Heather, pleased to be able to tell someone.

'Congratulations, Dawn. That's the final milestone before your exams. Why don't you go to break and get a drink? You need it, I can tell.' I thanked the staff nurse and made my way down to the canteen, beaming from ear to ear.

Almost there.

Chapter 20

Final Placement

At last, after a long road to qualification, I was on my final placement. After all the hard work that had gone into getting to this stage, including prior to my two-year conversion course, it was so good to be on the last leg. Somehow, I had always hoped I would get there, but never for a minute really thought it would come true.

It was my final week and I was working a split shift. No-one liked working split shifts; it felt like you might as well work the full twelve hours rather than have a few hours off in between. I had worked the morning part, which ran from 8am until 1pm, and the shift had gone well; all the patients on the ward were stable. There was no ward round due that day, so there were no consultant airs and graces to worry about. Some consultants were totally unreasonable and expected silence during their rounds, and some wouldn't do a round unless Sister was present.

On this particular day, I went to the hospital canteen prior to the second half of the shift and sat with a mug of coffee, thinking about what I would be doing after my holiday. Finishing up my coffee, I sighed and got up to go and see what the evening shift had in store.

Staff Nurse Loftus would be in charge – a quiet and efficient member of the team. We were due to be working alongside a first-year student called Carla. For some reason, she always looked scared to death and I couldn't help thinking she was going to be one of those who would drop out of training fairly quickly. There would also be two second-year students who were good workers, Mavis and Jo. During handover, we were told all the patients were stable, so we were looking forward to a rare busy but non-dramatic evening.

Once all the patients were settled and had evening drinks, it was time to write reports. I was twiddling my thumbs, wondering what to do next when I had an idea. I was due to leave the ward at the end of the week and there was a male nurse, Jack Maynard, who always ensured everyone who left was dumped in the bath fully clothed. It was a ritual that only occurred on this ward and only when Sister was not on duty. It would be my turn in a few days' time because Sister was off all week.

Perhaps the time had come for payback.

While Staff Loftus and Carla were at break, I hatched a plan with Mavis and Jo who would be working on Friday. Our only problem was that Jack Maynard was small in stature, but rotund, so our task would be difficult; we realised we didn't have enough brawn to manhandle him down a corridor. After considerable thought, we decided that one of the JHOs might just play ball.

As it happened, a patient rang his call bell to say he wasn't feeling that well. Mr Buchanan was suffering from a chest infection and did appear to be getting worse. His temperature had gone up from earlier and was reading 39°C, his heart rate was also high at 110 beats per minute and his respiratory rate was 24.

'I'll be alright, luv, don't worry about me,' he insisted.

'You have a high temperature, Mr Buchanan,' I explained. 'I need to call the doctor to check you over.'

'I don't want to be any trouble.'

'It's no trouble, Mr Buchanan.' *In fact, it's perfect*, I thought. Although I didn't wish the man to come to any harm, it was convenient.

I contacted the switchboard and asked for the JHO to be bleeped.

'Dr Connelly, the JHO, is on call and is coming to see Mr Buchanan,' I told my co-conspirators. 'We need to act quickly because Staff Loftus is due back any minute. Whoever doesn't get sent to break will need to ask him.'

Mavis looked concerned. 'What will happen if something goes wrong? We've still got a year to go.'

'The only thing that could go wrong is Staff Maynard snitching on us, but then we snitch in return. He's got too much to lose.'

'It's not that; it's just if harm comes to him, and then Sister finds out, we would be in trouble.'

'Yes, you're right,' I heard myself say. 'But this is happening with or without you, and think of all those girls he's dumped in the bath before.' Looking at Jo, I asked, 'How about you, are you in or out?'

The grin from ear to ear told me she had no issue with the plan. So, our plot was hatched. All we had to do was carry it out.

Dr Connelly duly arrived on the ward to examine the patient. It worked well because Staff Loftus sent me and Mavis for break so Jo was left behind. I suspected Mavis would have chickened out. When we got back to the ward, Dr Connelly had been and gone, having prescribed an intramuscular injection of amoxicillin for Mr Buchannan. Jo gave us a thumbs up on our return, so we were committed.

On Friday, my last day, I was excited for oh so many reasons, but mostly I hoped that my colleagues wouldn't back out of our plan and that it wouldn't be me who ended up in the lukewarm bath.

Jack Maynard was on duty and I could see his glee mounting at the prospect of dunking me as the day drew on. Mavis bleeped Dr Connelly, who arrived and hid in the bathroom. Maynard, true to form, wasn't willing to do any of his own dirty work – apart from manhandle student nurses, that is – and had ordered Jo to fill the bath ready. The time came and he grabbed me. He pushed me towards the bathroom, but as soon as we got in there, he was grabbed from behind by Dr Connelly, causing him to let go of me. The four of us then lifted him and dropped him unceremoniously into the colder than usual bath. We also shot a few syringes of calamine lotion at him for good measure and poured talc down his uniform.

He actually took it all in good humour and smiled sheepishly as he walked down the ward, dripping wet, with us following him and patients and visitors cheering us on. He did have the last laugh, though.

'Right, you lot, clear that mess up before any of you go off shift.'

We were an hour late leaving, but it was worth it and, apart from a few splashes, I was relatively dry. Thankfully, neither the Senior Nurse nor Sister ever found out, and Mavis and Jo didn't suffer any backlash from their part in my grand scheme.

A week later, a friend called me to let me know there was a letter from the English National Board for Nursing and Midwifery waiting for me. It had been sent to my old address, and she wondered whether it was my results.

'Yikes! I've been waiting for that, I did give them my new address.' I could feel my heart pounding through my chest.

'Do you want me to open it?' she asked.

I grimaced. 'Yes please.'

I waited for what seemed like an eternity, but was just a few seconds.

'Dear Miss Brookes, I have pleasure in informing you...'

Shrieks of joy from both ends of the telephone. I had done it – I was a registered nurse at last.

Thank you

Thank you for reading my third memoir. In order for me to gain feedback on whether you have enjoyed this book, and to hear any other thoughts you may have, I would love you to get in touch via either an honest review on Amazon or any other platform you use, or the contact form on my website. I am always looking to improve as both an author and a human being, and with that in mind I would appreciate your comments.

Dawn Brookes

To receive news and updates about my work, and the occasional 'no spam' newsletter, please join my reader group:

https://www.dawnbrookespublishing.com.

Connect with me via social media:

https://en.gb.facebook.com/dawnbrookespublishing/

https://www.pinterest.co.uk/dawnbrookespublishing/.

Hurry up Nurse

Memoirs of nurse training in the 1970s

The Interview – 1977

'Why do you want to be a nurse, Miss Brookes?'

Good question, I thought, but I knew I needed a decent answer. 'I would like to help people when they are at their most vulnerable, when they are ill,' I improvised. I couldn't really say, '*A friend told me I should be a nurse because I couldn't think of anything better to do, and she wished she had finished her training,*' even though that was nearer the truth. At least I had worked out that nursing involved caring for the sick. That statement and this interview were the beginning of the next thirty-nine years of my life.

The selection process for nursing was an all-day affair. I had written an application letter in January 1977 and was called for an interview in April. At the grand age of eighteen, I had never had an interview with more than one person before, and it was a bit daunting as there would be three people on the panel: what's worse, I didn't really know why I was there. I had no clue what nursing was all about.

First of all, I was shown into a room with a desk which immediately made me feel uncomfortable, reminding me of school days (my latter years at school hadn't gone well). I was a bit nervous, but felt quite good as I had dressed in my only decent clothes: a black skirt, white blouse, black jacket and tie (ok the tie bit is made up). After about five minutes a rather serious looking woman came in and introduced herself as Mrs Butcher though I was thankfully later to learn she was butcher by name not by nature; she was wearing a maroon uniform with a frilly hat and appeared to be in her fifties with round spectacles and a serious but not unkind demeanour.

'Good morning Miss Brookes. Before the interview "we" need to sit an entrance exam as we do not have the educational qualifications to be interviewed directly.' That really boosted my confidence. I was a bit confused as to why she needed to sit the exam too but didn't dare ask, and

I realised later that 'we' was the royal 'we' used by experienced nurses who often included it in their statements and questions: 'How are we today?' 'We are just going to have a little injection.' 'We are going to theatre today for an amputation aren't we?' and so on. Of course, many nurses were not looking for a reply to those questions at all. I bet many a patient wished the 'we' really did mean 'we'. *Focus Dawn,* I told myself, as I found myself daydreaming already. This had been my problem at school; there was always something more interesting to think about, hence my reports.

Hurry up Nurse 2

London Calling

I took one last look at my beloved bedsit in Leicester, partly to check I hadn't left anything behind and partly to say goodbye. It seemed silly being attached to a one-room bedsit, but I had spent two very happy years living there and was feeling irrationally attached to it at that moment.

Finally I sighed, whispered farewell, and looked at my rather large suitcase containing all my worldly possessions. It was an old brown suitcase that my mum had given me the week before when I had gone to say goodbye. A solid suitcase with two fastening clasps made of metal, a case that was of a type common in the 1970s. My mum had looked a little forlorn as I left, and I tried to make as light of it as possible, promising I would take care of myself and that I would visit when I could. London was only one hundred miles from Leicester but it may have been John o' Groats as far as my mum was concerned.

'Don't worry mam, I'll be fine and I will write and let you know how I'm doing.' Mum was doing her best not to show the sadness she was feeling and smiled as I left, but I knew she would cry when she went back inside the house.

It didn't pay to dwell on these morose thoughts though, and so I locked the bedsit door and dragged the suitcase down the stairs, sneaking past Casanova's flat on the ground floor and stepping outside into the fresh air. Casanova was a man in his mid-forties who constantly had women going in and out of his room at all times of day and night.

It was a bitterly cold Sunday morning in October 1980. I realised I wasn't dressed for the weather, as I had on a pair of light trousers and my favourite beige jacket; I immediately felt the icy cold wind blowing through my jacket and light silk blouse. *Oh well, too late now*, I thought, as all my clothes were in the suitcase and there was no way I was going to try opening it again after sitting on it that morning to make the clasps fasten. It had ended up being a battle of wills between me and the suitcase: I had finished up lying on it and getting it into a judo hold before finally managing to get one clasp to click into place. That had been followed by another monumental effort to get the other one closed. After shutting the front door leading into the house of bedsits that had been my home, I left my suitcase on the doorstep and popped down the road to post my keys through the landlord's door like he had asked me to.

I realised when walking back up the road how quiet it was on a Sunday morning. I looked across the road to the Charles Frears School of Nursing, the magnificent Tudor building where I had trained, and felt another sense of nostalgia. I arrived back at the house and half-carried, half-dragged the suitcase up the road to the bus stop. Thankfully, my bedsit had been fairly close to the main London Road and I crossed over with relative ease, as there was hardly any traffic around. By the time I got to the bus stop I was feeling a lot warmer due to the weight of my suitcase. For the first time that morning I was feeling excited about the adventure ahead of me and couldn't wait to get to London.

Acknowledgements

I couldn't have written this book without the help and support of my two best friends Ruth and Sue. Thank you for all the prompts and reminders that helped get this done.

I'm also grateful to readers of the other two memoirs who have encouraged (occasionally nagged) me to finish the third. I hope you enjoy the finished product.

Thanks once again to a marvellous editor, Alison Jack who always goes the extra mile and ensures a quality end product.

Thank you to friends & colleagues for your ongoing patience.

The biggest thanks goes to patients, past and present, because without you the world would have been a poorer place. Some patients referred to in this book are no longer with us but you are forever in my heart. I hope that you are now in readers hearts too even though they will never know your true identity.

About The Author

Dawn Brookes is a fun-loving, light-hearted person, with a creative side.

She writes across genres but has developed a passion for memoirs and cosy mysteries.

Dawn is author of the bestselling eBook *Hurry up Nurse: memoirs of nurse training in the 1970s* and *Hurry up Nurse 2: London calling*. She worked as a hospital nurse, midwife, district nurse and community matron during a career spanning thirty-nine years. Before turning her hand to writing for a living, she had multiple articles published in professional journals and co-edited a nursing textbook published by Palgrave Macmillan.

Dawn grew up in Leicester, later moved to London and Berkshire and now lives in Derby. She holds a Bachelor's degree with Honours and a Master's degree in education.

Dawn has a passion for nature and loves animals, especially dogs. Animals will continue to feature in her children's books as she believes caring for animals and nature helps children become kinder human beings.

Dawn is now writing full-time but is fitting in studying for an MA in Creative Writing.

Books by Dawn Brookes

Memoirs

Hurry up Nurse: Memoirs of nurse training in the 1970s
Hurry up Nurse 2: London calling
Hurry up Nurse 3: More adventures in the life of a student nurse

Rachel Prince Mystery Series

A Cruise to Murder
Deadly Cruise
Killer Cruise
Dying to Cruise

Coming Soon

A Christmas Cruise Murder

Sign up for my newsletter at
www.dawnbrookespublishing.com

Printed in Great Britain
by Amazon